Macmillan Building and Surveying Series
Series Editor: Ivor H. Seeley
          Emeritus Professor, Nottingham Trent University

Advanced Building Measurement, second edition   Ivor H. Seeley
Advanced Valuation   Diane Butler and David Richmond
An Introduction to Building Services   Christopher A. Howard
Applied Valuation   Diane Butler
Asset Valuation   Michael Rayner
Building Economics, third edition   Ivor H. Seeley
Building Maintenance, second edition   Ivor H. Seeley
Building Maintenance Technology   Lee How Son and George C.S. Yuen
Building Procurement   Alan E. Turner
Building Project Appraisal – Analysis of value and cost   Keith Hutchinson
Building Quantities Explained, fourth edition   Ivor H. Seeley
Building Surveys, Reports and Dilapidations, second edition   Ivor H. Seeley
Building Technology, fifth edition   Ivor H. Seeley
*Civil Engineering Contract Administration and Control,
    second edition*   Ivor H. Seeley
Civil Engineering Quantities, fifth edition   Ivor H. Seeley
Civil Engineering Specification, second edition   Ivor H. Seeley
Computers and Quantity Surveyors   A.J. Smith
Construction Contract Claims   Reg Thomas
Contract Planning and Contractual Procedures, third edition   B. Cooke
Contract Planning Case Studies   B. Cooke
Design-Build Explained   D.E.L. Janssens
Development Site Evaluation   N.P. Taylor
Environmental Science in Building, third edition   R. McMullan
Greener Buildings – Environmental impact of property   Stuart Johnson
Housing Associations   Helen Cope
Housing Management – Changing Practice   Christine Davies (Editor)
*Information and Technology Applications in Commercial
    Property*   Rosemary Feenan and Tim Dixon (Editors)
Introduction to Valuation   D. Richmond
Marketing and Property People   Owen Bevan
Principles of Property Investment and Pricing   W.D. Fraser
Property Valuation Techniques   David Isaac and Terry Steley
Public Works Engineering   Ivor H. Seeley
Quality Assurance in Building   Alan Griffith
Quantity Surveying Practice   Ivor H. Seeley
Recreation Planning and Development   Neil Ravenscroft
Resource Management for Construction – An integrated approach
    M.R. Canter
Small Building Works Management   Alan Griffith
Structural Detailing, second edition   P. Newton
Urban Land Economics and Public Policy, fourth edition
    P.N. Balchin, J.L. Kieve and G.H. Bull

(continued)

Urban Renewal – Theory and Practice   Chris Couch
1980 JCT Standard Form of Building Contract, second edition
  R.F. Fellows

Building Project Appraisal

Analysis of value and cost

Keith Hutchinson

Department of Construction Management and Engineering
University of Reading

First published 1993 by
THE MACMILLAN PRESS LTD
Houndmills, Basingstoke, Hampshire RG21 2XS
and London
Companies and representatives
throughout the world

ISBN 0–333–57834–1

A catalogue record for this book is available
from the British Library.

Printed and bound in Great Britain by
Biddles Ltd, Guildford and King's Lynn

Contents

Preface   ix

1   Introduction   1
  1.1 Purpose   1
  1.2 Meaning of the Term 'Developer'   1
  1.3 Financial Appraisal   2
  1.4 Building Projects   2
  1.5 Need for Joint Appraisal of Cost and Value   2
  1.6 Effective Project Cost Management   3
  1.7 Computer Programs   3
  1.8 Outline of Contents   4

2   Development Budget   5
  2.1 Definition   5
  2.2 Outline of Budget's Main Elements   6
    2.2.1 Project Value   6
    2.2.2 Project Costs   6
    2.2.3 Price   6
    2.2.4 Project Viability   7
  2.3 Uses and Purposes of the Development Budget   7
    2.3.1 Determination of Project Viability   7
    2.3.2 Establishment of Cost Limits for Particular
    Budget Elements   7
    2.3.3 Establishment of Project Management Cost
    Targets   8
  2.4 Accounting for Time in the Development Budget   9
    2.4.1 Effect of Time on Budgeted Amounts   9
    2.4.2 Compounding and Discounting   10
    2.4.3 Compounding and Discounting: Examples   11
    2.4.4 Choice of Rate in Compounding and
    Discounting Calculations   14
  2.5 Accounting for Inflation in the Development Budget   15
  2.6 Further Reading   16

3 Development Process   **17**
   3.1 Outline of the Development Process   17
       3.1.1 Inception: Decision to Build   17
       3.1.2 Acquisition of Land   18
       3.1.3 Planning and Building Permission   18
       3.1.4 Design   19
       3.1.5 Construction   19
       3.1.6 Commissioning   19
   3.2 Methods of Procurement of Design and Construction   20
       3.2.1 Introduction   20
       3.2.2 Traditional Procurement   20
       3.2.3 Design and Build   21
       3.2.4 Management Contracting   23
       3.2.5 Construction Management   24
   3.3 Effect of Procurement Method on Total Cost of the
       Project   24
   3.4 Effect of Procurement Method on Project Cost
       Management   25
       3.4.1 Project Cost Management Using Traditional
             Procurement   25
       3.4.2 Project Cost Management Using Design and
             Build Procurement   26
       3.4.3 Project Cost Management Using Management
             Contracting and Construction Management
             Procurement   28
   3.5 Further Reading   28

4 Project Value   **29**
   4.1 Introduction   29
   4.2 Methods of Forecasting Project Value   29
       4.2.1 Basis and Derivation of Available Methods   29
       4.2.2 Method 1: Comparable Sale Value   30
       4.2.3 Method 2: Current Capital Value   33
       4.2.4 Method 3: Capitalised Income   35
       4.2.5 Method 4: Target Value   37
   4.3 Uses of Methods of Determination of Project Value   40
       4.3.1 Introduction   40
       4.3.2 Uses of Methods in Different Development
             Situations   41
   4.4 Summary of Use of Methods of Calculating Project
       Value   47
   4.5 Taxation: Effect on Project Value   47
   4.6 Further Reading   49

5 Project Cost   **51**
  5.1 Cost Items   51
      5.1.1 Land Acquisition Costs   52
      5.1.2 Relocation Costs   52
      5.1.3 Construction Costs   53
      5.1.4 Commissioning Costs   54
      5.1.5 Finance Costs   54
      5.1.6 Taxation   56
  5.2 Analysis of Building Cost   56
      5.2.1 Introduction   56
      5.2.2 Builder's Resource Costs   57
      5.2.3 Builder's Price   61
  5.3 Forecast of Builder's Price at Development Budget
      Stage   63
      5.3.1 Basis of Development Budget Building Cost
            Forecast   63
      5.3.2 Building Price Forecast by Floor Area   64
      5.3.3 Other Methods of Forecasting Building Price   68
      5.3.4 Price-forecasting for Alteration/Refurbishment
            Projects   70
      5.3.5 Price-forecasting External Works   71
  5.4 Further Reading   71
      Appendix A to Chapter 5: Operational Building
      Work Sections   72
      Appendix B to Chapter 5: Quantified Work Items   73
      Appendix C to Chapter 5: Example of Unit Rate
      Resource Cost Calculation   74
      Appendix D to Chapter 5: Example of Calculation of
      Project Overhead Cost   74
      Appendix E to Chapter 5: Building Price Index   75
      Appendix F to Chapter 5: Design Elements   76

6 Project Feasibility   **77**
  6.1 Introduction   77
  6.2 Methods of Determination of Project Feasibility   78
      6.2.1 Balance of Realised Value and Incurred Cost   78
      6.2.2 Balance of Present Value   78
      6.2.3 Rate of Return   83
  6.3 Suitability and Use of Methods of Determination of
      Feasibility   85
  6.4 Further Reading   85
      Appendix A to Chapter 6: Resource Use Profile for
      Typical New Build Construction Project   86

Appendix B to Chapter 6: Feasibility Calculation Using
Present Value Method   86

7 **Project Risk: Analysis and Management**   89
  7.1 Introduction   89
  7.2 Quantification and Presentation of Risk in the
      Development Budget   90
      7.2.1 Statistical Probability   91
      7.2.2 Sensitivity Analysis   95
      7.2.3 Simulation Technique   96
  7.3 Management of Risk   96
  7.4 Further Reading   98
      Appendix A to Chapter 7: Sensitivity Graph – Effect
      on Rate of Return of Variation to Forecasts   98

Appendix: Compounding and Discounting Tables   99

Index   105

Preface

The task of writing this book was commenced under the influence and, in some instances, the inspiration of past professional experiences and acquaintances. Now that the task is finished I can more easily identify those experiences, views, opinions and practices of colleagues that have shaped the book and thus can give the acknowledgements and thanks that are properly due.

During my practice as a quantity surveyor I was involved, at various levels, with many different types of developer and building project. I thus saw many different methods and procedures used for budgeting and controlling the cost of development projects. These varied in style from that of pressing on regardless in hope and faith that things would be alright in the end, to that of an obsessive need to identify and record precisely every event that affected cost, however insignificant. This obsession, I noticed, often increased in intensity with the decrease of cost significance of the event. These variations in style initially puzzled and ultimately interested me with respect to their methods, purposes and results. When my professional activities turned to teaching on degree level courses in building management and surveying, this necessarily involved a closer and more analytical consideration of the methods that I had encountered during my professional practice.

The students I have met and taught during my educational activities are perhaps the prime cause of my desire to write this book. Degree level education in quantity surveying is, in terms of educational subject development, a new activity, particularly so in its part-time mode which was initially my first involvement in the process. Thus the students suffered the inevitable fog of uncertainty that surrounds any new activity. I was impressed by and admired the way they faced and found their way through the gloom. They generally appeared to be less daunted than I felt myself to be. I hope this book will be of use or interest to those of my ex-students, now in practice, who suffered the effects of my own feelings of uncertainty.

The dominant influence on the form and content of this book is the work of Professor Ivor Seeley. He wrote the first book which identified and defined the constituent topics and practices for the subject of building economics. This book set the scene for an essential development which is still taking place, that is, the evolution of the role of the quantity surveyor to that of the specialist, technical accountant and cost manager of the building development process. Professor Seeley's book and the professional acquaintance I was privileged to make with him were influences without which I would not have been able to consider writing this book. I am also grateful to him for the advice he gave me while I was planning and writing it.

I would like to thank all my present and past colleagues who have spared me their time for the discussions which have contributed to the content of this book, and in this respect I would expressly mention Mike Canter, Andy Forgan, Tom Putt, Professors Brian Atkin and Roger Flanagan.

I would also like to thank all those people who gave me assistance with the vital technical processes of completing the manuscript (or diskette as now, perhaps, more properly it should be called), particularly Moira Gill, Tina Jeffrey, Ann Skinner and John Jewell.

I am grateful to the Royal Institution of Chartered Surveyors and the Building Cost Information Service for their permission to extract material from their publications for use in this book.

University of Reading   Keith Hutchinson
January 1993

1 Introduction

1.1 PURPOSE

Source

Books, papers and lectures concerned with the general subject of building costs are frequently introduced with a biblical exhortation that anyone contemplating a building project ought to give serious consideration to the cost of doing so and the availability of the resources to meet these costs (*St Luke* 14, verse 28). As excellent as this advice is, it only goes part of the way in a contemporary, economic context. For a building developer needs to consider not only the cost of a proposed project but also whether that expenditure is worth incurring. That is, the developer must consider the completed project's value. Value and cost are the determining factors in the viability of a proposed building project, and the analysis of these concepts is the purpose of this book.

The aim is to describe and explain the principles of the techniques that a developer can use to appraise the financial viability of undertaking a building project. The form of presentation of these techniques is the process of the developer's initial decision about whether or not to undertake the project.

This decision can be made by developers on the basis of varying qualities of informed data and varying levels of formality depending on the nature and extent of the proposed building project and the nature and requirements of the developer. This book attempts to identify and describe the best and latest techniques for producing the most meaningful data on which to base the decision to build, and assess the appropriateness of the different techniques for the varying circumstances in which building work could be required or desired.

1.2 MEANING OF THE TERM 'DEVELOPER'

The term *developer* is used throughout this book to include any person, organisation, body or authority that undertakes the process of commissioning building work for whatever purpose, be it use or sale or for commercial profit-making or private motives.

1

1.3 FINANCIAL APPRAISAL

The usual, dominant factor in the consideration of the decision about whether or not to build is of course financial viability and this is so whether the developer is a profit-making, commercial organisation or one whose objective is not profit. However, this is not the only factor. Other considerations in the decision about whether or not to build, such as environmental quality, are of course important, but go beyond the scope of this book, which is concerned solely with a project's financial viability to the developer.

1.4 BUILDING PROJECTS

The term *building projects* is used in this book to include all construction work in the widest possible sense. As well as new building work it includes those alterations and refurbishments of existing buildings that go beyond merely repair and maintenance work. Any construction work that has an ascertainable value and a cost to a developer is a building project within the defined term of this book. Construction projects that are excluded from this definition and are not susceptible to the value and cost ascertainment techniques described are civil engineering, public works projects – the essential value of these being public utility rather than individual utility for a particular developer. The techniques of assessing this wide public value are not included in this book.

1.5 NEED FOR JOINT APPRAISAL OF COST AND VALUE

It is a significant purpose of this book to include in one text several different topics which traditionally have been dealt with separately under different, professional disciplinary headings. Usually in the development process in the UK a potential developer who requires expert professional advice on making a decision about whether or not to undertake building work needs to consult various professional advisers – for instance, a financial analyst for advice on the revenue obtainable from the project, a property valuer for the likely selling price or capital value, a quantity surveyor for the likely construction cost, an accountant for the cost of financing the project, a building surveyor for the likely maintenance requirements and a facilities manager for the likely occupancy costs. Expert textbooks exist on all these disciplines and techniques. It is the intention of this book to describe them all and, most importantly, demonstrate the need for and method of integrating their operation.

One advantage of this integration of the whole appraisal exercise into one operation is the improved and more meaningful character that this gives to the appraisal. The decision that is based on the appraisal can be taken with more confidence if its essential elements, that is, cost and value, have been assessed and quantified with full cognisance of each other. All the factors in the appraisal can then be considered in their entirety and the most sensitive elements recognised by one specified individual. The construction industry and property professions should be able to offer any potential client developer a complete appraisal service for any type of development. To be able to do this, the traditional disciplinary functions need to be integrated.

1.6   EFFECTIVE PROJECT COST MANAGEMENT

The need for effective project management which ensures the achievement of the developer's financial and quality objectives for the project is now recognised in the UK construction and development industry. To carry out the project management task properly the project manager requires a meaningful budget that expresses the targets of the project and serves as a management tool. A properly integrated cost and value appraisal will provide this.

The initial development appraisal cannot serve as a meaningful budget if it consists of diverse sets of separately derived calculations for which no single professional consultant is in a position to take responsibility. Too many development budgets represent hopeful aspirations combined into an overall result on which none of the separate consultant parties have their sights fully set. A project manager or lead consultant who has prepared an integrated project appraisal and developed this into a realistic target development budget will be in a good position to achieve its aims. Such a project manager will know the overall effects on the development budget of all occurrences in the design and construction process and, most significantly, will be able to take amending action to reset the project to its overall target when these occurrences adversely affect the original budget provisions.

An understanding of all the development budget and appraisal elements is required to facilitate effective management action in directing the project to its overall targets. It is an aim of this book to provide such required, overall understanding.

1.7   COMPUTER PROGRAMS

Most of the particular calculations and techniques described in this book can be carried out by individual computer programs. Programs are also beginning to be developed which can carry out the overall appraisal exercise which is this book's subject. However, the development of these programs comes from general investment appraisal techniques and commercial property development appraisals; thus they tend to emphasise an approach based on the needs of commercial property developers. They require further development to make them of general applicability for all types of developer as defined earlier. Such development of these computer programs has yet to take place. Construction industry professionals need to be able to provide a service of appraisal for all their potential customers.

1.8 OUTLINE OF CONTENTS

To achieve the aims and purposes previously stated, the book will describe the methods and practices which can be used to determine and quantify the financial factors which govern project value and cost, and the techniques that can be used to relate these two basic elements of project viability. In order to do this it will also describe and explain how the costs and incomes that are forecast and budgeted are actually incurred or realised so as to assist full understanding of the forecasting techniques. The context in which these costs and revenues are incurred and realised, that is, the development process, consisting of inception, planning, design, construction and maintenance, will be described. The alternative procedures that can be used for this process will be considered, particularly with respect to how these alternative procedures can affect the incurring of cost.

It is hoped that this book will be of practical use to potential developers and project managers for gaining an understanding of how an appraisal and development budget should be prepared and its aims achieved. It should also be of interest to all building professionals and students of building for an understanding of the economics and financing of building projects.

The individual techniques described are worthy of specialist study in addition to their need for integration. Reference is given in appropriate chapters to specialist texts on these topics and techniques.

2   Development Budget

2.1   DEFINITION

The development budget is the statement of the financial viability of a proposed building project as represented by a forecast of the project's value and cost and an appraisal of the relationship between these two elements.

This appraisal of a proposed project's financial viability needs to be undertaken at the inception of the project. Thus the forecasts of cost and value which make up the development budget are also required at this early stage. At this inception stage the data and information available to make the necessary forecasts of cost and value may be limited or incomplete. However, using appropriate techniques and specialist knowledge, it is possible and desirable to produce, even at the inception stage, a development budget which fulfils the functions required of it as detailed in section 2.3. The budget can be developed as further information and data are received during the early stages of the project.

An example of the elements of a development budget follows. In this example, the classifications of cost are broad and only illustrative.

Outline Example of a Development Budget

Developer: Light electrical goods production company.
Proposed project: Construction of new factory for proposed new production line.

Forecast project value (millions of £)	*Forecast project costs (millions of £)*
5.135	1.75 Land acquisition
	2.45 Construction
	0.05 Relocation
	0.75 Finance
	5.00 Total

5

2.2   OUTLINE OF BUDGET'S MAIN ELEMENTS

2.2.1   Project Value

The value of the project is the utility or benefit of the completed project to the developer, expressed in financial terms.

The most meaningful method of establishing this amount is dependent on the nature of the developer and the intended use of the completed project. For example, the developer may intend selling or renting the completed project for commercial profit; or the intention may be for the developer to utilise the building for his own activities, the ultimate purpose of which is, again, commercial profit. A developer whose purpose is not commercial profit will usually utilise the building himself to achieve his desired aims.

In all these situations, value is a distinct concept and requires different methods of quantification. These methods and their uses are considered in detail in Chapter 4.

2.2.2   Project Costs

Project costs are all the expenditures incurred by the developer in completing the project to the condition for which a value was calculated.

All building projects have costs which go beyond just the costs of the developer. There are costs to the public and the community in terms of environmental quality, and general economic costs in terms of the effect of the work on the supply of resources. These are important and should always be considered by a developer. However they will not be considered in this book which, in this development budget context, is only concerned with the developer's direct financial costs of the project or, to define them in a different way, the costs of a project that the developer cannot avoid paying.

The costs identified in the example development budget just given are a broad classification of possible project costs within this definition, and these are analysed in more detail in Chapter 5.

2.2.3   Price

This term will be used to refer to the charges made against the developer by suppliers of services which are required for completion of the project. For example, the charge made by the seller of land to the developer and the charge made by the general contractor for the management and execution of the building works are prices in the above sense.

These prices represent developer's costs, of course, as defined above in section 2.2.2. It is important, for an understanding of cost forecasting and control techniques, to recognise and analyse these costs in terms of the price mechanisms which govern them. This analysis is covered in Chapter 5.

2.2.4 Project Viability

Viability refers to the financial feasibility of undertaking the development of the proposed building project. It is determined by the relationship of project value, as defined in section 2.2.1, and project cost, as defined in section 2.2.2.

A simple method of determining viability by this relationship is to decide that if value exceeds cost then the project is viable. The project illustrated in the example development budget in section 2.2.1 would be viable on this basis. This method, however, fails to account for certain important factors that would influence viability. These include the risk and uncertainty of the forecasts being accurately fulfilled, the profit or return required by the developer, the time at which the value of the project will be realised and the costs of the project incurred. These factors and the methods of assessing them in the appraisal of the relationship between cost and value are covered in detail in Chapters 6 and 7. The principle of the techniques for dealing with time in development budgets is considered in section 2.4 of this chapter.

2.3 USES AND PURPOSE OF THE DEVELOPMENT BUDGET

2.3.1 Determination of Project Viability

This result, achieved as described in section 2.2.4, is the core purpose of the development budget. It is the basis on which the decision about whether or not to build is made.

A frequent refinement towards this end is to use the budget to appraise the relative viability of alternative projects that are under consideration. If the decision to build has been made in principle, further decisions may be required on the nature of the project to be undertaken. Separate development budgets representing the alternative proposals under consideration can be prepared. The decision as to which of these proposals will be undertaken will be determined by the relative relationships of the different values and costs of the alternative proposals. The techniques which can be used for this purpose are described in Chapter 7.

2.3.2 Establishment of Cost Limits for Particular Budget Elements

The purpose of this is to establish how much can be expended on a particular development cost item. It is essential that all other cost items and the project value are forecastable, and that the required relationship between value and total cost has been determined. When these items are known or forecastable the limit of cost for the required cost item, which will result in the required profit or return for the project, can be ascertained.

The usual situation for this use of the development budget is in commercial property development where it is needed to determine the allowable amount which can be expended on the purchase of land for a proposed project. When a proposed project is outlined in terms of its cost, excluding land, its value and required return, then the budget can be utilised to produce the amount which can be paid for a suitable piece of land. The value produced by this technique is usually referred to as the *development value* of the land, and the technique itself as *residual valuation*.

2.3.3   Establishment of Project Management Cost Targets

A development budget when approved by a developer represents the financial aim of the proposed project in terms of the cost/value relationship. For commercial developers this financial aim will usually be expressed in terms of a level of profit or rate of return. The individual components of the budget elements, that is, the constituents of the project value and the budget cost items, can thus be viewed as *the means of achieving the financial aims of the project and as targets for achievement by the project's management.*

The majority of the individual budget items included in the development budget are forecast amounts. The actual realisation and achievement of these amounts will be in the future, and in the nature of development projects there will always and inevitably be differences between the forecast amounts and the actual amounts. This does not, however, negate the use of the development budget as a management tool for achieving the project's overall aim. Two techniques, both expanded upon in later chapters, can be used to give the development budget its ability to be utilised to secure the achievement of the project's financial objectives.

Firstly, the risk and uncertainty which prejudice the forecasts of the budget can be quantified, to a limited extent, and expressed in the budget. This draws them to the attention of the project's management and allows for the making of preparatory provision for the occurrence of an unfulfilled forecast.

Secondly, the budget's elements can be checked, monitored and reconciled against the actually incurred costs as the project proceeds, and necessary amending action taken to compensate for the unfulfilment of a forecast budgeted element. For example, a higher than forecast land acquisition cost can be compensated by a reduction in construction cost. This will not adversely affect the overall project aim, provided the reduction in construction cost does not affect project value and should be possible if the construction cost forecast was properly and expertly carried out. The checking, monitoring and reconciling process should be given top priority by management. Cost planning and control at the design stage are essential in this respect.

A properly cost-managed project will achieve its overall aim although there will inevitably be some variations to the planned course, as set out in the development budget, before this destination is reached.

2.4 ACCOUNTING FOR TIME IN THE DEVELOPMENT BUDGET

2.4.1 Effect of Time on Budgeted Amounts

The development budget in its basic form, as illustrated earlier in section 2.1, consists of a schedule of financial amounts of total project costs and revenue, in the form of the project value. The amounts are forecasts of actual amounts to be paid or received by the developer. In this form the budget takes no account of the financial effects of the time of their payment or receipt. The project programme will determine when the costs are to be incurred and paid, and when the value is to be realised and received. Very few, if any, developments are such as to result in a single point of costs and receipt of value. The actual profile over the time period of the project of the meeting of costs and receipt of value is referred to as the project's *cash flow*. The projects's cash flow profile must be reflected in the development budget, because time has a significant effect on the real value of a cost or revenue receipt.

The effects of time on the real value of monetary amounts can be expressed simply as follows. A value realised at a later point in time than originally envisaged is a lesser real value. Five pounds to be received in twelve months' time is worth less than five pounds to be received next week. Equally, a cost paid at a later time is a lesser cost. Five pounds to be paid in settlement of a debt in one year's time is a lesser cost than five pounds which is due next week. The converse of these two statements is equally true: a value realised earlier than expected has a greater real value, and a cost paid earlier is a greater real cost.

The mechanism which produces this effect is predominantly the investment potential of money as expressed by the charge that is usually made on the lending of money in the form of an interest rate charge. A person in possession of a sum of money can increase its amount by investing the money. The investment can consist of the owner lending the money to someone to engage in a commercial profit-making venture and charging him or her for the service, or the owner of the money himself engaging in a commercial profit-making venture. In both cases the original sum (the capital) will grow with the addition of either the owner's profit on his activity or the charge he makes to the borrower (the interest).

Thus five pounds owned now will have a greater value in one year's time because interest will have accrued to it. Conversely, five pounds to be received in one year's time will have a lesser value now because no interest will accrue since the five pounds is not earning interest for its future owner.

Development budgets must account for this adjustment made to budget amounts for the time profile of cost and value. The detailed techniques for doing this are covered in the appropriate chapters on project value, project cost and project viability. The general principles of the techniques follow in this chapter.

2.4.2 Compounding and Discounting

Converting a sum of money to account for the time of its payment or receipt involves adjusting the sum by two factors. Firstly, the appropriate rate of interest which is expressed as a percentage for a given term and is usually referred to, in this context, as a discount rate and, secondly, the length of the term, that is, the length of time which is applicable to the particular adjustment.

The adjustments can take two forms: (1) calculating the amount to which a presently held sum of money will accumulate over a period of time, referred to as the *future compounded amount*; (2) calculating the present equivalent amount of a sum that is to be acquired or spent in the future, referred to as the *present value*. Both of these amounts, future compounded amount and present value, are derived from application of the two factors identified above, that is, the discount rate and the appropriate term, to the amount to be adjusted.

These calculations can be carried out by the application of the appropriate mathematical formulae or by use of published tables of discounted and compounded values for given rates and terms. The former of these can now be performed quickly and easily by calculators or computer programs. Tables are still in common use, however, and summary tables which will be required for the examples below and other calculations in this book are given in the Appendix.

The examples below illustrate the most common form of discounting and compounding calculations required in development budgets. For simplicity, all these examples are based on a discount rate of 10% per annum. The factors affecting the choice of this rate are considered in section 2.4.4.

2.4.3   Compounding and Discounting: Examples

(1) Calculation of the Compounded Amount of Presently Held or Expended Sum

A developer has paid £150 000 for land for building. What is the real value of this expenditure after 10 years, assuming an interest rate of 10%?

This requires the compounding of £150 000 for 10 years at a rate of 10% per year. The formula for the compounded amount of £1 is:

$$(1 + i)^n$$

where i = rate of interest expressed as a decimal value, that is,
       10% = 0.1
   n = total term at the rate of interest.
The formula can be calculated and applied to the £150 000, thus:

$$£150\ 000 \text{ at } 10\% \text{ p.a. for } 10 \text{ years} = 150\ 000 \times (1 + 0.1)^{10}$$

$$= 150\ 000 \times 2.5937$$

$$= £389\ 055$$

Alternatively, the compounded amount of £1 for 10 years at 10% p.a., that is 2.5937, can be found from the appropriate discount table instead of using the formula. See 'Amount of £1' table in the Appendix. The factor from the table is applied to £150 000, as above.

In the calculation above, the sum of £389 055 represents the amount to which £150 000 will accumulate (capital + interest), if invested at 10% per annum rate of interest for 10 years. Thus it can also be said to represent the accumulated value in ten years' time of an expenditure now of £150 000, if the rate of interest or the owner's expected rate of return on capital expenditure is 10%.

(2) Calculation of the Present Value of a Future Sum of Expenditure or Received Payment

A developer expects to sell a house, which is being built, for the sum of £150 000 in 3 years' time. What is the present value to the developer of this sum of £150 000 to be received in 3 years' time, assuming an interest rate of £10% per annum?

This requires the discounting to a present value of the amount of £150 000 at the rate of 10% per annum for the term of 3 years. The formula for the discounting to present value (PV) of £1 is:

$$\frac{1}{(1 + i)^n}$$

where the values of *i* and *n* are as in Example (1).

This formula can be calculated and applied to £150 000 thus:

$$\text{PV of £150 000 at 10\% for 3 years} = 150\,000 \times \frac{1}{(1 + 0.1)^3}$$

$$= 150\,000 \times 0.7513$$

$$= \underline{£112\,695}$$

Alternatively, the present value of £1 in 3 years at 10%, calculated by the formula above, that is 0.7513, can be found in the 'Present Value of £1' table in the Appendix, and the factor applied to £150 000.

In the calculation above, £112 695 represents the amount which if invested now at a rate of interest of 10% for 3 years will accumulate to £150 000. Thus it also represents the present value of the receipt or payment of £150 000, in 3 years' time, if the rate of interest is 10%.

(3) Calculation of the Compounded Amount of a Series of Equal Regular Payments

A developer will spend £15 000 each year on maintenance and heating of factory units. What will be the compounded value of the total expenditure after 10 years, assuming an interest rate of 10%?

This requires the compounding of the amount of £15 000 annually for 10 years at a rate of interest of 10%.

The formula for the compounded amount of £1 per annum is:

$$\frac{(1 + i)^n - 1}{i}$$

where the values of i and n are as in Example (1).

The formula can be calculated and applied to the £15 000 thus:

$$\text{£15 000 per annum at 10\% for 10 years} = 15\ 000 \times \frac{(1 + 0.1)^{10} - 1}{0.1}$$

$$= 15\ 000 \times 15.9374$$

$$= \underline{£239\ 061}$$

Alternatively, the amount of £1 per annum for 10 years at 10%, that is 15.9374, can be obtained from the appropriate table. See 'Amount of £1 per period' table in the Appendix.

In the calculation above, £239 061 represents the amount to which £15 000 invested annually will accumulate (Capital + Interest) at an interest rate of 10% after 10 years. Thus it can also be said to represent the real value of an annual expenditure of £15 000 for 10 years if the spender expects to earn a 10% return on investment.

(4) Calculation of the Present Value of a Regular Series of Future Expenditures or Received Payments

As in Example (3), a developer will spend £15 000 each year for 10 years on heating and maintenance of factory units. What is the present value of the future expenditure assuming an interest rate of 10%?

This requires the discounting to a present value of the annual expenditures of £15 000 for 10 years at the rate of 10% per annum.

The formula for the discounted present value (PV) of £1 per annum is:

$$\frac{(1 + i)^n - 1}{i(1 + i)^n}$$

where the values of i and n are as in Example (1).

This formula can be calculated and applied to the £15 000 per annum for 10 years:

$$\text{PV of £15 000 p.a. for 10 years} = 15\ 000 \times \frac{(1 + 0.1)^{10} - 1}{0.1 \times (1 + 0.1)^{10}}$$

$$= 15\ 000 \times 6.1446$$

$$= \underline{£92\ 169}$$

Alternatively, the PV of £1 p.a. for 10 years at 10%, that is, 6.1446, calculated by the above formula, can be obtained from the tables. See 'Present Value of £1 per period' table in the Appendix.

In the calculation above, £92 169 represents an amount which if expended now is the equivalent of expending £15 000 annually for 10 years, assuming that a 10% rate of return is expected on capital investment.

Examples (3) and (4) can be used to illustrate the relationship between the concepts of actual values, compounded equivalent values and present equivalent values.

In these examples the *actual* value of the developer's expenditure is £150 000, that is, £15 000 annually for 10 years. The *compounded equivalent* value of this expenditure is £239 061. The additional amount represents the interest that the developer would have gained by investing the amount rather than expending it on the maintenance. The *present equivalent* value of this expenditure is £92 168, the reduction from the actual amount representing the interest that the developer should gain on the amounts of the actual expenditure that remain in his possession during the 10 year term.

The Present Value of these expenditures can also be calculated from the compounded equivalent value, thus:

Compounded equivalent value = 239 061
× PV of £1 in 10 years at 10%   0.38554

Present Value   = £92 168

Discounting and compounding can be summarised in the following way. Actual amounts of expenditure or received income can be adjusted to express their real value taking account of the time of their payment or realisation by:

(1) Compounding a present amount to its future equivalent. This means adding the amount of interest or return that the amount would have earned over the term of its expenditure.
(2) Discounting a future amount to its present equivalent value. This means discounting the amount of interest or return that would have been earned if the amount had been available for the period from the present to the time of its actual receipt or expenditure.

2.4.4   Choice of Rate in Discounting and Compounding Calculations

The rate used in these calculations is clearly of crucial significance to the resulting adjusted real value, and thus of similar importance for the determination of project viability embodied in the development budget. Therefore a meaningful rate must be used in the budget. The correct rate depends on the particular situation of the developer, the project and the current economic conditions because, in most situations, the rate reflects the lost opportunity to the developer of earning a return on an amount of capital that is expended on the project or a receipt of income that is deferred. In this sense the rate chosen should reflect the developer's expected or required return on capital investment and is thus a question for the developer's individual stipulation.

It may be impossible for some developers to stipulate with any certainty such a rate of return either required or expected, particularly if the developer is not a commercial organisation. In these situations what is required is a forecast of an appropriate rate. Such forecasts can be made in two ways. Firstly, on the basis of current returns or yields on specified types of investment. This involves an analysis of current returns on Government Stock (Gilts) or current yields in the developer's area of operation and the current market rates of interest. Secondly, if the developer is not a profit-making organisation, the rate should reflect the rate of interest that the developer will pay for borrowing on the basis of current market rates.

Further consideration is given to this aspect in Chapters 4 and 6.

2.5 ACCOUNTING FOR INFLATION IN THE DEVELOPMENT BUDGET

The budget consists of a schedule of project costs and a project value, which is determined in many cases on the basis of incomes produced by the completed project. All such future costs and incomes will be subject to the effects of inflation, that is, the economic phenomenon of rises in prices or falls in the purchasing value of money over time. This can be accounted for in the budget in two ways.

Firstly, the costs and incomes which determine the budget's values can be adjusted directly for a forecast inflation rate before being input to the budget calculations. Discounted cash flow techniques of appraisal of the budget, which are explained in Chapter 6, particularly facilitate this method of accounting for inflation and will be fully considered in that chapter.

Secondly, the costs and incomes can be input to the budget calculations on the basis of forecast *current* cost and price levels. The effects of forecast inflation can then be included by an adjustment of the discount rate that is used to adjust the resulting amounts for their time profile. The merit of this technique lies in the commonly used method of making the choice of discount rate on the basis of current levels of interest rates. As stated above, if the choice of discount rate cannot be based on an actually required or expected developer's rate of return then current interest rates can be used as a good indication of an appropriate rate. As the level of the market rate of interest is one which reflects and includes an allowance for the inflation rate, then this technique has a theoretically sound basis. If the discount rate chosen is the market rate of interest it will thus adequately make the necessary adjustment for forecast inflation.

However,the technique of discount rate manipulation to make allowance for uncertain or unpredictable factors should be avoided where possible, and separate adjustment of costs and incomes for inflation using a discounted cash flow technique is the better technique. The main reason for this is that, as will be made clear when cost forecasting techniques are examined in detail in Chapter 5, the direct input of an adjustment for inflation provides a more readily identifiable management cost target and thus greater facility for effective cost management.

2.6 FURTHER READING

Bennett J., *Construction Project Management*, chapter 6. Butterworths, 1985.

Britton W., Davies K. and Johnson T., *Modern Methods of Valuation*, 7th edn, chapter 8. Estates Gazette, 1989.

CIOB, *Code of Practice for Project Management in Construction*. CIOB, 1992.

Davidson A., *Parry's Valuation and Investment Tables*, 11th edn. Estates Gazette, 1989.

Ferry D.J. and Brandon P.S., *Cost Planning of Buildings*, 6th edn, chapters 1–4. BSP, 1990.

Isaac D. and Steley T., *Property Valuation Techniques*, chapter 4. The Macmillan Press, 1991.

Marshal P.J.L. and Yates A., 'Development appraisal', in *Quantity Surveying Techniques: New Directions* (Ed. Brandon P.S.). BSP, 1988.

Pilcher R., *Project Cost Control in Construction*, chapter 2. BSP, 1985.

Seeley I.H., *Building Economics*, 3rd edn. The Macmillan Press, 1983.

Walker A., *Project Management in Construction*, 2nd edn, chapter 7. BSP, 1990.

Yates A. and Gilbert B., *Appraisal of Capital Investment in Property*. Surveyors Publications, 1991.

3 Development Process

3.1 OUTLINE OF THE DEVELOPMENT PROCESS

This section describes the procedures typically required for the building development process in the UK. The term *building development process* is used here to mean the commissioning of the planning, design and construction of a new building or the alteration of an existing building.

The precise nature of the procedures that are used for this process will determine the time at which its value is realised and the time and method of incurrence of its costs. The most significant parts of the process, in this sense, are those of procuring the design and construction of the project, and these will be given more detailed consideration, in section 3.2, following an outline of the whole development process.

3.1.1 Inception: Decision to Build

The decision to build is the decision that a perceived need can be satisfied by the construction of a new building or the alteration of an existing building. The making of such a decision necessarily requires, firstly, the identification of the nature of the need and, secondly, the formulation of the required performance of the new building or alteration of an existing one that will satisfy it.

It is the identification of these needs and the formulation of the means of their satisfaction which allow the preparation of the initial development budget and provide the data for the forecasts of costs and value which are its key elements.

At the inception stage, this data will not be precise or detailed. But, as will be explained when the techniques of value and cost forecasting are explained in later chapters, it is possible to produce a meaningful development budget at this stage. Moreover it is essential as well as possible to do so; for the preparation of a realistic, meaningful development budget at this stage will prevent the developer incurring

17

any unnecessary abortive costs in pursuit of a project that is discovered financially unviable at a later stage. In addition, there is no reason why a development budget prepared at this initial stage should not have the required characteristics, identified in Chapter 2, to allow the budget to represent the management targets.

3.1.2   Acquisition of Land

This process is the acquisition by the developer of a suitable tenure in real property which allows the development of a building that satisfies the identified need of the developer.

If this acquisition requires expenditure, it is a process that will not be entered into without a high degree of certainty with regard to the financial viability of the project. The achievement of this certainty is one function and purpose of the development budget prepared at the inception stage. In addition, some certainty will be required, before expenditure on land acquisition, with regard to the likelihood of obtaining the approval of the Planning Authority for the proposed development (see section 3.1.3).

3.1.3   Planning and Building Permission

New building work will generally constitute 'development' within the meaning of the planning legislation, and will thus require an application to and approval from the Local Planning Authority for the project. Building work which consists of the alteration of an existing structure will require the same Planning Authority approval when it constitutes a 'material change of use' of the building.

Planning approval for a development project can be obtained in stages. Firstly, outline approval can be obtained which approves and permits the concept of the project, that is, its nature, function, size and basic form. Secondly, detailed approval is required which covers the project in its proposed completed form. Thirdly, Building Regulation approval is required, which confirms the construction and specification details of the building in terms of the statutory requirements of standards of safety, stability and comfort embodied in the Building Regulations.

In many development situations, the first of these approval stages may be the one which triggers the developer's decision to build, and will thus precede the inception stage described in the previous section, or at least be concurrent with it. The second and third of these stages will occur later in the whole process, as they are necessarily postponed until some considerable design work has been undertaken. The development budget forecasts must therefore take full account of the likely requirements of the local authority in regard to their planning consents and building regulation approvals, which will have cost and value significance.

3.1.4 Design

Design is the process of translating the developer's needs into a proposed building. The stages of the completed design process can be classified into the following three broad activities:

(1) Developer's brief. This is the formulation of the developer's performance requirements for the project in terms of its required function and the standards which will affect the execution of this function.
(2) Outline design. This is the determination of the form of the building in terms of shape, height and number of storeys which will fulfil the developer's performance requirements and comply with any constraints that are particular to the project and its situation.
(3) Detail design. This is the formulation of the proposals for the technically complete achievement of the building's form and performance requirements.

The programming of the execution of the design process in the whole development process will be determined by the procurement method chosen for the project. However, whatever the method of procuring the design of the project used, the developer's brief is required at the earliest stage of the project, because it is an essential component, at least in outline form, of the preparation of the development budget.

3.1.5 Construction

This consists of the processes of manufacture, assembly and site operations and their planning, organisation and management, which are required for the conversion of the designed project into an actual building.

3.1.6 Commissioning

This term is used to include any processes required to be undertaken to the constructed building to allow the developer to utilise it for the planned purpose. The nature of any commissioning processes will depend on the nature of these planned purposes.

A developer whose intention is sale or disposal of the building may need to commission selling agents and lawyers for this process. One whose intention is use of the building may require it to be fitted out or installed with specialist equipment required for the particular intended use.

All buildings require maintenance, heating, power provision, occasional repair and management of their facility throughout their life cycle. These processes are beyond the description of the development process used in this chapter. However these processes will be a cost to a developer who does not sell or dispose of the developed building, and are an important element of the development budget in that they are one of the determinants of the project value. This will be considered in detail in Chapter 4.

3.2   METHODS OF PROCUREMENT OF DESIGN AND CONSTRUCTION

3.2.1   Introduction

Procurement method means the project management system and contractual arrangements used by the developer to secure the design and construction services required for the execution of the proposed project to the required quality for the required cost and within the required time. The relative efficiency of the various possible procurement methods in achieving these aims is not considered here except in so far as they affect the possible techniques for forecasting cost and value for the preparation of the development budget and its successful implementation. For this latter purpose, the current commonly used procurement methods are described with particular reference to the effects they may have on the incurring of project costs and the scope they give for management cost control.

The different procurement methods considered are:

1. Traditional procurement
2. Design and build
3. Management contracting
4. Construction management

3.2.2   Traditional Procurement (Table 3.1, Part 1)

The traditional, and probably still the most common procurement method is one whose most significant feature is the carrying out of design and construction as two distinct, separately and consecutively executed, processes. The two processes are undertaken by separate parties under contract to the developer.

The design process will be undertaken by a professional designer, usually an architect, who will have overall responsibility for the process and its organisation. Specialist design services, if required by the nature of the project, will be provided by appropriate specialists, under contract to the developer and under the organisational supervision of the lead designer, the architect. Such specialists might include a structural engineer, mechanical and electrical engineers and a quantity surveyor for design cost input.

The construction process, its execution, planning and management will be undertaken by a general building contractor, who will make a contract for this with the developer on the basis of the design of the work as completed by the architect. This means that no construction work can commence until the design is complete, as it forms the basis for the contract price and work content and, consequently, the general contractor who is to manage and execute the construction operations is excluded from the design process. The contract is usually made on the basis of price competitive bids from a number of selected general contractors. The general contractor is contractually responsible to the developer for completion of the whole of the construction work. But most general contractors engage works contractors, to carry out specialist parts of the works under contracts negotiated by the general contractor and the individual works contractors. These sub-contracts have no direct effect on the developer's subsequent actual cost for the work. The developer pays the general contractor's agreed price for the construction work.

Supervision of the quality of the general contractor's work is usually undertaken by the designer, the architect. The administration and settlement of the financial terms of the contract between the developer and the general contractor is carried out by the quantity surveyor.

Using the traditional procurement method, the developer's cost for design and construction of the project consists, typically, of:

(1) Design fees. These include the price charged by the architect for design and quality supervision of the construction work, the prices charged by any specialist designers, and the price charged by the quantity surveyor for design cost advice.
(2) Construction cost. This consists of the general contractor's agreed tender price, including adjustment for variations and adjustments within the terms of the agreed contract.
(3) Financial administration cost. This is the quantity surveyor's price (fee) for administration of the competitive tender for the construction works and settlement of the developer's contract with the general contractor.

3.2.3 Design and Build (Table 3.1, Part 2)

This procurement method integrates the two process of design and construction, which characterised the traditional method by their separation, into the responsibility of a single party: a design/build

Table 3.1   Functions and contractual arrangements under alternative procurement methods

1. TRADITIONAL METHODS

↔ = *Contract*

DEVELOPER

Architect
Design
Quality
supervision

Specialist Designers
Services etc.
design
Services etc.
quality supervision

Quantity Surveyor
Design cost
control
Financial
settlement

General Contractor
Construction

Works Sub-contractors
Site operations

2. DESIGN AND BUILD

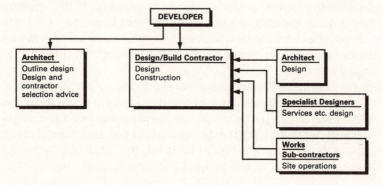

DEVELOPER

Architect
Outline design
Design and
contractor
selection advice

Design/Build Contractor
Design
Construction

Architect
Design

Specialist Designers
Services etc. design

Works Sub-contractors
Site operations

3. MANAGEMENT CONTRACTING

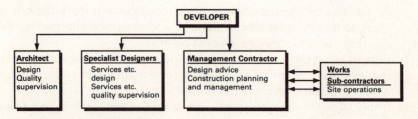

DEVELOPER

Architect
Design
Quality
supervision

Specialist Designers
Services etc.
design
Services etc.
quality supervision

Management Contractor
Design advice
Construction planning
and management

Works Sub-contractors
Site operations

4. CONSTRUCTION MANAGEMENT

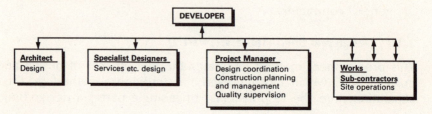

DEVELOPER

Architect
Design

Specialist Designers
Services etc. design

Project Manager
Design coordination
Construction planning
and management
Quality supervision

Works Sub-contractors
Site operations

contractor. The design/build contractor undertakes the process of design, based on the developer's requirements, and the execution, planning and management of the construction process under contract to the developer for a single agreed price.

The contract for design and construction is often made after a competitive tender between several design/build contractors. This, of course, cannot be based solely on price, but design consideration and quality will also be factors in the choice. For this reason, developers using this system often engage a professional architect to advise on selection and, less often, a quantity surveyor to advise on price negotiation. An architect will also often be engaged by the developer to prepare the employer's requirements on which the design/build contractor will base the design.

Although the essential characteristic of this system is the integration of the entire design and construction process into the single point responsibility of one design/build contractor, it is usual for that contractor to engage specialist professional designers to undertake the design function under contract to him. Also, as general contractors usually operate under the traditional system described above, the design/build contractor will usually sub-contract parts of the execution of the works to specialist works contractors. These sub-contracts will have no direct effect on the developer's actual total cost for the design and construction of the project. The developer will pay the design/build contractor the agreed price for design and construction of the work.

Using the design and build system the developer's cost for the design and construction of the project will, typically, consist of:

(1) The design/build contractor's agreed price.
(2) The developer's consultant architect's charge for preparation of the developer's requirements for the project and advice on contractor selection.

3.2.4 Management Contracting (Table 3.1, Part 3)

The characteristics of this procurement method is the identification of three functional elements of the design and construction process and a contractual arrangement which aims to reflect the required status and role of the parties who execute these functions. The three functions are:

(1) Design.
(2) Building planning, organisation and management.
(3) Building work operations.

The developer engages a designer and a management contractor at an early stage of the project. The designer undertakes the design of the project with input from the management contractor. The management contractor undertakes the planning, organisation and management of the construction operations as well as providing design input. The construction operations are carried out by specialist works contractors, who are chosen by the developer, or his design and management team. The works contractors execute their work under contract to the management contractor, although the terms of these works contracts, with regard to price and work content, will be determined by the developer's design and management team.

The developer's costs under this procurement system consist of:

(1) The designer's fee.
(2) The management contractor's charge. This will consist of a fee for the planning, organisation and management function, which will usually have been obtained by a competitive tender, plus the amounts paid by the management contractor to the works contractors.

3.2.5   Construction Management (Table 3.1, Part 4)

This method has the same underlying basis as management contracting in that it seeks to achieve the early appointment of a design and project management team, which includes the party responsible for the management of the construction process. To this end, a designer and a construction manager are appointed at an early stage, prior to the commencement of detail design. The difference between this system and management contracting is that the works contractors are engaged to carry out the site work under contract to the developer rather than the management contractor.

The developer's costs under this system will consist of:

(1) The designer's fee.
(2) The construction manager's fee.
(3) The tender prices of the works contractors.

3.3   EFFECT OF PROCUREMENT METHOD ON TOTAL COST OF THE PROJECT

The relative merits of the various systems with regard to their management effectiveness in achieving the project aims is not discussed here. However, the different methods do have, as has been shown, varying levels of effectiveness in securing quality of construction and achievement of time goals and these, particularly the latter, will affect project cost. The programmed time for construction significantly affects the project's real value and real cost. The method of accounting for this in the budget is shown in Chapter 6.

Another factor affecting project cost in the chosen method of procurement is the effect that the method may have on the prices obtained by works contractors, general contractors and designers, and how these are translated into developer's costs. Making allowance for this at the development budget stage may be difficult in that the choice of procurement system may not have been made at this early stage of the project. This is further discussed in Chapter 5.

3.4 EFFECT OF PROCUREMENT METHOD ON PROJECT COST MANAGEMENT

Perhaps more significant than the effect of the procurement system on total cost is its effect on the facility of the method to allow for effective cost management, that is, the monitoring, reconciling and amending of actual costs with forecast costs in the development budget.

The effectiveness of a procurement system in allowing proper cost management depends on, firstly, at what stage and to what extent certainty of costs, that is, the confirmation of forecast costs, is obtained and, secondly, what scope exists in the system for amending planned future costs to correct cost deviations between actual costs and budget forecasts.

Each of the procurement systems described previously will now be considered with respect to these two requirements for effective cost management.

3.4.1 Project Cost Management Using Traditional Procurement (Table 3.2, Part 1)

Using a traditional procurement system, with competitive tenders invited for the construction work, a substantial certainty of construction cost (and thus design costs which are usually directly tied to it) should be obtained at the stage of receipt of tenders, which is usually a relatively early stage in the overall project programme. The contract made on the basis of the tender, if fixed price, represents a substantially certain indication of final construction cost. This is so, provided the design on which the tender is based is in reality complete and the contractor's tendered price is realistic.

Failure in the first of these provisos would result in variations to the contracted work and a consequent adjustment to the contractor's price. This produces a significant uncertainty as to the ultimate actual cost. The application of the traditional procurement system is usually characterised by a far from complete design at tender stage and thus, in practice, the system is usually characterised by the uncertainty caused by the need for variations to the contracted work.

Failure to ensure a contract sum based on a realistic tender sum can result in either insolvency of the general contractor or slow progress owing to poor cash flow. The delays caused by both of these consequences produce considerable uncertainty of final actual cost.

Scope for correcting amendment of budget elements in response to actual cost variations is limited using traditional procurement.

Before tenders are received, no construction cost certainty is present, so there is no perceived need for amendment, except for the design problems that are encountered during the design process which may prejudice the accuracy of the budget's construction cost forecast. The application of design cost planning and control techiques can alleviate such problems. Indeed, design cost planning and control, if properly and competently carried out, will reduce the likelihood of the tender price exceeding the budgeted amount as well as assisting in mitigating problems that arise at design stage.

After the tender for construction is received there is scope for amendments to design and a negotiation of a contract price within the budgeted figure, provided the overrun of the forecast construction cost is not too substantial. Redesign can cause an extension to the programme, which results in an unbudgeted cost however, and should always be allowed for in the budget adjustment.

After the contract is made, when cost certainty is high, the scope for any cost amendments is limited by the costs that result as the consequence of variations, mentioned above.

3.4.2 Project Cost Management Using Design and Build Procurement (Table 3.2, Part 2)

Using this procurement method, very substantial certainty of design and construction cost can be obtained at the stage of making the design/build contract, and this stage can be reached relatively earlier than under a traditional method. The potential design/build contractor or competing contractors can be provided with the budget figure, which clearly assists in achieving its target in the obtained contract sum.

When the contract is made, the uncertainties of variations due to incomplete design, which are a characteristic of traditional procurement, are not the cost responsibility of the developer and thus do not produce uncertainty for the developer's budget. However, variations made by the developer to the original brief on which the design/build contract was made can cause considerable cost increase. Scope for

Table 3.2   Outline programme of alternative procurement methods indicating levels of cost certainty and facility for project cost amendment

- - - - Level of cost certainty
------- Level of cost amendment scope

1. TRADITIONAL METHOD

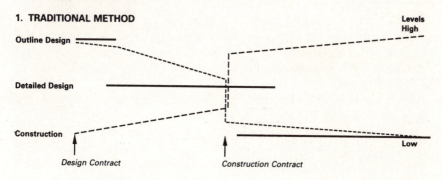

2. DESIGN AND BUILD

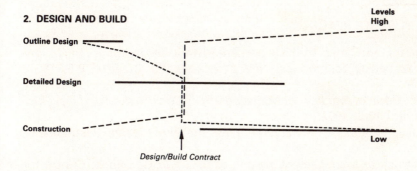

3. MANAGEMENT CONTRACTING AND CONSTRUCTION MANAGEMENT

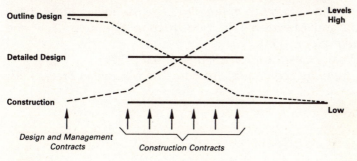

amendment of budget elements after the contract has been made is limited by this cost of variations to the design build contract.

3.4.3   Budget Cost Management Using Management Contracting and Construction Management Procurement (Table 3.2, Part 3)

These two procurement methods have the common characteristic of the contracts for the work execution, which represents the bulk of the construction cost, being made in stages during the design and construction programme. For cost management purposes, this has the effect of reducing and delaying the achievement of cost certainty, but increasing and extending the scope for making amendments to budgeted targets.

When each of the contracts for the individual work sections are made, they can be monitored against and reconciled with the targets budgeted for these in the development budget and design cost plan. As detailed design will still be proceeding, any necessary amendments can be made to compensate for the non-fulfilment of targets for completed work sections. Although, of course, the facility for this will depend on the extent of the cost overrun and the quality of the design cost plan.

3.5   FURTHER READING

Bennett J. and Grice T., 'Procurement systems for building', in *Quantity Surveying Techniques: New Directions* (Ed. Brandon P.S.). BSP, 1988.

CIOB, *Code of Practice for Management in Construction and Development*, CIOB, 1992.

Cornick T., *Quality Management for Building Design*. Heinemann, 1992.

Construction Management Forum, *Report and Guidance*. Centre for Strategic Studies in Construction, University of Reading, 1991.

Ferry D.J. and Brandon P.S., *Cost Planning of Buildings*, 6th ed. BSP, 1990.

Griffith A., *Quality Assurance in Building*. The Macmillan Press, 1990.

Hughes W.P. and Murdoch J.R., *Construction Contracts: Law and Management*. Spon, 1991.

Pilcher R., *Project Cost Control*, chapter 5. BSP, 1985.

Seeley I.H., *Building Economics*, 3rd edn. The Macmillan Press, 1983.

4 Project Value

4.1 INTRODUCTION

The subject of this chapter is the determination of the value of the completed project to its developer and the methods and techniques that can be used to represent this value as a financial amount that can be included in the development budget. The project value is the developer's credit element in the development budget account. It is the amount against which the forecast project cost (Chapter 5) is balanced in order to appraise financial viability of the project (Chapter 6) and to set management targets for the achievement of the project's financial aims.

Value is a subjective concept and there are different ways in which it can be financially quantified. The most appropriate method in a given development situation is the one that most meaningfully represents the developer's purposes for and utilisation of the intended, completed project. Thus the choice and use of a method of calculating a value for a project will depend on the nature of the developer and the purpose of the project.

This chapter will firstly describe, illustrate and comment upon the various methods of determining a project value, and then relate these to the different, possible types of development situation, with the intention of indicating the appropriateness of use of the different techniques.

4.2 METHODS OF FORECASTING PROJECT VALUE

4.2.1 Basis and Derivation of the Available Methods

The classified methods to be described are largely derived from general, investment appraisal techniques and, more particularly, from property valuation techniques used by professional surveyors for the purpose of estimating the value of an interest in property, as they have been developed and applied for use in commercial property development appraisals.

The relevance of these techniques to forecasting a value for an intended building project is clearly close, for a completed building project represents 'an interest in property' for the developer. However, the development of the techniques has largely concentrated on the needs of one particular type of developer, namely the commercial property developer, that is, a developer undertaking a building project for the purpose of sale or lease as a commercial investment. This is narrower than the definition of developer used for this book (Chapter 1), thus it does not provide a comprehensive analysis of value for all development situations. What is required for use in development situations as generally defined is a clear and meaningful representation of value in order that the development budget can fulfil its purpose as a cost management tool.

Thus the methods described are aimed at synthesising, adapting and adding to the techniques of property valuation and investment appraisal with the purpose of providing methods for use in all development situations that will be of use in the practical application of the function of project cost management. Such methods are classified here as:

(1) Comparable sale value
(2) Current capital value
(3) Capitalised income value
(4) Target value

These methods are described in the following sections, with illustrative examples of their application in calculations.

4.2.2   Method 1: Comparable Sale Value

This method consists of representing the project value as the amount that the developer would obtain if he sold the property interest in the completed project.

This sale value is ascertained on the basis of past or current sale/purchase transactions in properties or buildings similar to that of the project, known as 'comparables'. This produces a market value for the building, which is defined in the context of professional property valuation as the price which would be obtained on an open market, with a willing seller and purchaser and no special considerations affecting the transaction.

The comparable properties used to derive a market sale value for a project must be ones of similar type to that of the project. For this purpose, the classification of buildings in identifiable, specialist property markets can be used. Such clear and identifiable markets are those for housing, commercial (offices), retail (shops) and industrial (factories, warehouses, etc.) properties.

Even within these classified, well-identifiable and recorded property markets, the market values which they produce require adjustment with regard to the particular circumstances of the project for ascertaining its comparable sale value for a particular project. Such circumstances which will affect the sale value of the project within the market includes location, quality standard, physical building condition and fluctuations over time in supply and demand in the market.

The size of the building will also affect its sale value within the market. This can be adjusted by using values for *quantified units* of comparable buildings. The units quantified will be those appropriate to the function of the building and thus ones that are particularly value sensitive. The most appropriate unit for commercial and industrial buildings is the usable floor area. Similarly, retail buildings can be unit quantified on the basis of usable floor area, although an additional vital value factor in such buildings is the length of the building frontage, and this requires consideration when ascertaining a value from a comparable. Appropriate units for housing are bed-spaces or bedrooms.

The sale value of a comparable building, or the aggregate sale value of comparable buildings, is converted to a sale value per unit, which is then applied to the quantified units of the project considered to obtain a total sale value.

A summary formula for the Comparable Sale Value method can be expressed thus:

Project Value = Market sale unit value of comparable building
$$\times$$
Project unit quantity
$$\times$$
Adjustment for variable factors of project:
location
quality standard
condition of comparable building
market fluctuation

The market sale unit value is ascertained most accurately from an aggregate of comparable buildings where there is a clear market, with many recorded transactions. This requires adjustments for particular circumstances of location, quality standard and condition of comparables to be undertaken accordingly.

An example of application of the above method, in this case using just one comparable property, is now illustrated.

Proposed project: Light, industrial factory building with usable, productive floor area of 6000 m^2, in city suburban location on main trunk road.

Comparable: Factory, built 25 years ago for light industrial production, with productive, usable floor area of 4000 m², situ-
ated on main trunk road; sold at auction 2 years ago for
£2.5 million. Inflation in the industrial property market
has been 3% in the 2 years since sale.

Calculation of comparable sale value:
The appropriate, comparable unit for such buildings is the productive,
floor area m². The unit value of the comparable building is thus:

£2.5 million divided by 4000 m² = £625 per m²

This unit value can be used to calculate the project value:

6000 m² at £625/m²   = £3.75m

Further adjustments are required for:

Comparable condition + 1%	0.0375
	3.7875
Market inflation (3% per annum)	
× Amount of £1 at 3% for 2 years	1.0609
	4.0182
PROJECT VALUE	£4.0 million

This value is the current sale value. The development budget will
require this amount to be adjusted for the value at the time at which it
will be actually realised, that is, when the project is complete and
commissioned. This adjustment will be considered in Chapter 6.

The use of the comparable sale value method depends for its use on
the existence of an identifiable market for the type of building being
valued, with access to reliable data on market transactions. This may
make the method unusable for building development projects other
than those which come within the markets of housing, commercial,
industrial and retail property previously identified. Its use is also subject to resolution of the philosophical question of whether buildings,
which are all unique, can be considered comparable in any meaningful
way.

The appropriateness and use of the method is considered below in
section 4.2.3.

4.2.3   Method 2: Current Capital Value

This method represents the value of a development project as its capital value on completion. The capital value of an asset is the financial amount which quantifies the income-earning potential of the asset and the rate of profit return, or yield, required by the owner of the asset.

This is traditionally the most commonly used method of valuing interests in income-earning property, existing or potential, and is usually known as the *investment method*. The capital value of the property interest is calculated from the net periodic income that the property could earn, usually in the form of rent, and the periodic rate of return or yield that the investor requires or expects to receive on capital investment, which will be, in this case, expenditure on the acquisition of the property interest.

The method is used to ascertain a *current* capital value, with the income-earning capacity of the building used in the calculation being the currently obtainable income from such buildings. The rationale for the use of this form of the method is that buildings have a long-term life expectancy and the prediction of income over this span is impossible to predict with any certainty. In this form, the method is often used to calculate a market sale value of the property. For certain types of building, primarily commercial office buildings, the market sale value can be considered equivalent to the current capital value, provided that the yields derived from such property closely follow the market.

The basis of the method can be expressed in the following way.

The value of a proposed project is its current capital value. The current capital value of a project is the amount which if invested in the form of expenditure on the procurement of the project would produce a given, periodic rate of return from a given periodic income from the project.

This can be understood by considering, firstly, the concept of a periodic rate of return. This consists of the amount of the periodic, usually annual, income obtained from an investment in a capital asset expressed as a percentage of the amount of the capital investment. For example, the investment of £100 in the procurement of an asset which earned £10 in the first year of ownership would produce a rate of return of 10% for that first year's period. This can be expressed in the formula:

Periodic rate of return(%) = (Periodic income ÷ capital sum)
                                                × 100

Thus for the example
above:
Annual rate of return(%)   = (10 ÷ 100) × 100
                                      = 10%

This formula for calculation of the periodic rate of return on a capital investment can be transposed to produce a formula for calculation of the current capital value. Thus:

Current capital value   = (Periodic income ÷ periodic rate
                             return (%)) × 100

However it is more accurate, when applying this formula to calculate a current capital value, to multiply the periodic income by the factor which discounts a future periodic income flow, for the total term of the income flow, at the rate (%) of the required return, to a present value, instead of dividing by the rate of return. This was explained in Chapter 2, section 2.4.

Thus the formula for calculating the capital value of a future income flow is:

Current capital value   = Periodic income × PV of £1 per
                             period at periodic rate of return (%)
                             in perpetuity

An example of the application of the method is now illustrated.

Proposed project: Commercial office building with net lettable area of
                     2000 m². Current net rent income from comparable
                     office buildings is £50 per m² and current rate of
                     return is 8%

Calculation of current capital value:

Capital value   = Net periodic income × Present value of
                   £1 per period at periodic rate of return
                   in perpetuity
                 = (2000 m² × £50/m²) × PV of £1 per annum at 8%
                   in perpetuity.
                 = 100 000 × 12.5
                 = £1.25 million

This calculation effectively discounts to a present value the receipt of an annual income of £100 000 in perpetuity at a rate which equates to the profit – a rate of return that the developer requires on capital investment, that is, the yield, which in this case is 8%.

Certain aspects of this calculation are, of course, notional. The first of these is the use of the current income as the actual income for the full period of the building's earning potential. This can be accepted on the basis that it gives a *current* capital value at the time when the income level used was current. If income rises in the future then the current capital value will rise at the time of the income rise. Falls in income would have the opposite effect on capital value. However, allowance is often made in these calculations for the risk of not realising the forecast income used in it. As this risk cannot be precisely quantified, the allowance is made by adjusting the discount rate used in the calculation. Raising the rate to allow for the possibility of not realising the forecast income, for example by the occurrence of voids in letting a rented property, would have the compensating effect of lowering the capital value.

A second notional element of the calculation is the use of perpetuity as the period of income receipt from the building. This constitutes the only method of allowing for a value factor which cannot be quantified precisely, the value factor being whatever is the value of the building at the end of its effective income-earning life.

The principle of the method is appropriate for those building developments, the purpose of which is to generate a long-term, potential income flow, which cannot be precisely actualised nor realistically forecast.

4.2.4 Method 3: Capitalised Income

This method represents the value of the building as its capital value. This, as defined in section 4.2.3, is a quantified amount based on the income-earning potential of the asset and the required rate of profit return on investment in the asset. However, the distinction between this method and the current capital method previously described is that this method is based on the capitalisation of *actual* income rather than current incomes projected forward to give a current, future variable value.

The value of the building is represented by the present, capitalised value of the actual net incomes that will be generated by the project during its life cycle. These actual net incomes are capitalised to a present value using a discount rate which represents the developer's required rate of profit return.

The principle of calculating a present, capital value of a building project on the basis of the forecast, actual, future incomes that the project will generate can be illustrated by the following example.

Proposed project: Alteration work to an existing factory, production building, which will increase net income by £10 000 per year for five years. The developer requires a rate of return on investment of 5%.

Calculation of project value:

		£
Project net annual income × PV of £1 p.a.	=	10 000
for 5 years at 5%		4.3295
	Project value =	£43 295

    The significant feature of this method is the use in the capitalisation process of actual incomes of the project. This involves a more complex calculation than the single figure used in the example shown previously, for the method requires the identification of a significantly precise projection of the amounts of the incomes and costs of the project and its utilisation, and the time profile of their receipt and incurrence. This is undertaken by the preparation of a cash flow schedule of the project's incomes and costs.

    The items which will appear in the schedule of incomes and costs of a project can be classified as follows:

(1) Project operating income
This is the revenue that the developer gains from the operating purpose or function of the project. Depending on the nature of the developer this will usually only be obtainable from the developer's specialist analysis.

(2) Project operating cost
The costs incurred by the developer from the operation of the project. Like the operational income this will be dependent on the developer's specialist analysis.

(3) Building facility costs
These are the costs of ownership or occupancy of the building, consisting of utility provision, structure and fabric maintenance, and structure and fabric repairs. These costs can be identified by professional building design and surveying techniques and accounted for by the use of life cycle costing techniques.

(4) Residual cost/income
The costs incurred or income derived by the disposal of the building project and the land at the end of its project life cycle.

    A schedule of income and costs identifying the above possible items and the time of their occurrence in the life cycle of the building project is a complex task. The following example simplifies the extent of the items to illustrate the principle.

Proposed project
The construction of a warehouse storage facility by an industrial manufacturing company. The facility will be built on land owned by the
company and will be required for ten years. The company currently
store the materials, for which it now intends to utilise the facility, in a
warehouse for which it has a five year lease at a rent of £20 000 per
year. This rent is expected to rise to £25 000 per year when the company renews the lease for a further five year period. Maintenance and
service costs for the new warehouse will be £3500 per year at current
prices. Redecoration, the current cost of which is £1150, will be required in years 4 and 8 of the project's life. The building will be
demolished at the end of its life cycle. The current cost of demolition
of such buildings is £10 000. The rate of price inflation over the life of
the project is expected to be 3%. The company require a rate of return
of 5% per year on capital investment.

A value for the above project can be ascertained, on the basis of the
present capital value of the net yearly values of the incomes and costs
of the project. The income in this case consists of the saving achieved
by removal of the need to rent a storage facility. A calculation of a
project value on this basis requires the preparation of an income and
cost schedule, which produces the annual cash flows of the project.
The total of these annual net incomes is discounted to a present value
at the rate of 5%, the developer's required rate of return (see Table
4.1).

The capitalised income method requires that the incomes and costs
of the project can be precisely identified and realistically forecast. This
requirement can make the method inappropriate for projects with long
life cycles, for the level of precision and reliability of forecasts over
such periods is not sufficiently high. Cost and price inflation are significant factors in the uncertainty of future incomes and costs.

4.2.5 Method 4: Target Value

All the methods of ascertaining a project value described above were
based on quantifying the project's future financial benefits to the
developer in the form of potential realisation by sale or generation of
income. Not all projects have such potential, or if they do, it may not
be such as to facilitate quantification. It can be argued that such
projects have no financial value, particularly if the developer is not a
profit-making organisation.

However, it is essential that all projects are given a financial value.
Such a value is necessary for ensuring effective cost management,

Table 4.1   Project capitalised income value

| YEAR | REVENUE | COSTS | | | NET CASH FLOW | PV of £1 at 5% | PV |
| | (£) | (£) | | | (£) | | (£) |
	Rent-saving	Main-tenance	Decor-ation	Demo-lition			
0	20 000	3500	1150	10 000			
1	20 000	3605			16 395	0.95238	15 614
2	20 000	3713			16 287	0.90703	14 773
3	20 000	3824			16 176	0.86384	13 973
4	20 000	3939	1294		14 767	0.82270	12 149
5	20 000	4058			15 942	0.78353	12 491
6	25 000	4179			20 821	0.74622	15 537
7	25 000	4304			20 696	0.71068	14 708
8	25 000	4434	1457		19 109	0.67684	12 934
9	25 000	4567			20 433	0.64461	13 171
10	25 000	4704		13 439	6 857	0.61391	4 210

Total Present Value   £129 560
PROJECT VALUE   £130 000

control and monitoring, and efficient economic performance in the land acquisition, design and construction processes. A financial value is required against which to set and target the costs of these activities. In the sense of a target against which to balance project costs, value is the most appropriate term, or more particularly target value.

The technique described below does not constitute the financial representation of a realisable value, but is a mechanism for ensuring that the costs incurred by undertaking the project achieve value in the broadest sense of that term.

The basis of the technique is to establish a value for the project by reference to and analysis of past projects which made comparable provision to that of the proposed project. Comparable projects, for this purpose, can be past projects by the developer or other organisations.

The most meaningful way of determining the comparability of previous projects is in terms of the *function* of the building. The cost of the comparable projects is most meaningfully expressed in terms of the functional unit provision made by the past projects. The most appropriate functional unit is the one that most closely represents the purpose of the building's function. For example:

Building function	*Functional unit*:
Housing	Bedrooms
Education	Pupils/students
Hospitals	Patients/beds
Religious	Worshippers
Administration	Floor area
Recreation/leisure	Floor area

The cost of a past comparable project, or a mean cost of past projects, expressed in terms of functional units, can be used to set a target value for the proposed project. In order that this method does not merely constitute a self-fulfilling exercise of ascertaining a value target which, in reality, merely constitutes an estimate of cost, it is necessary to analyse and make adjustments to the historic functional cost or costs of the selected comparable projects. For this purpose, the comparable project costs should be broken down into categories which have significantly different, variable cost factors. Broadly, the two most significant items in the total cost of a typical project, as considered in detail in Chapter 5, consist of acquisition of land and design/construction costs. The cost of past projects should separately identify the cost of these two items for the purpose of analysing and making adjustments to the target value.

The following are factors which should be considered when adjusting the functional cost of past projects to produce a meaningful target value for the proposed project.

Particular Cost Factors

Any circumstances which would have affected the costs of the comparable project or projects that have been used to derive a value of the proposed project and that will not apply to the proposed project should be identified, quantified and discounted from the target value assigned for the proposed project. Such circumstances include the following:

(a) Market conditions. A developer's cost for the acquisition of land and procurement of design and construction will be significantly affected by the conditions of supply and demand in the markets for these items. This should be accounted for when obtaining a project value on the basis of past costs. The plus or minus difference that the market conditions will produce between the comparable project and the proposed project should be allowed for so as to obtain a value on a basis common to that of the past project. The conditions of the markets in land and design/construction will vary, which necessitates the breaking down of the past project costs referred to previously.

(b) Design constraints. Features of the specification or form of the building which are determined by the particular circumstances of the project should be adjusted in the assigned target value. Examples of such features are the required life of the building, environmental factors, service level provision or features of the land which affected form, shape and structural provision of the building. Such features may exist in the past comparable building or the proposed project. In either case an adjustment is required in order to ensure that the target value derived reflects as closely as possible the value of a function that is common to the past project and the proposed one.

(c) Functional appraisal. Where the assigned project target value is to be based on the cost of one past project, an architectural and services analysis should be made of that project to assess the effectiveness of the building in achieving the performance of its function. An identified under-achievement in this function in the past project requires an adjusting increase in the target value for the proposed project.

4.3   USES OF METHODS OF DETERMINATION OF PROJECT VALUE

4.3.1   Introduction

The most appropriate method of determining the value of a proposed building project will depend on the nature of the developer and the intended purpose of the project. There are various different types of developer within the definition used in this book and these may undertake a building project for different purposes. Therefore, every project must be considered in the context of its particular circumstances when making the choice of an appropriate method of ascertaining the development budget value. The significant aim of the development budget is to relate the costs of the project to its realised value, therefore the method of determining value should be chosen in close consideration of this aim.

In order to illustrate the principles to apply in this selection of a method, developers and their project purposes have been broadly classified in the following way:

(1) Property developer
(2) Business organisation developing a project for:

    (a) identifiable income generating purposes
    (b) general operating efficiency purposes
(3) Non-business organisation developing a project:
    (a) to be financed by income generated by the project itself
    (b) to be financed from general funds

This classification is broad and many developers or development situations may have elements which include more than one of the categories. Its intention is to illustrate the principles to apply when selecting an appropriate project value determination method. In the following sections the methods are considered for each of the broad development situations identified, with further explanation of the situations themselves.

4.3.2 Uses of Methods in Different Development Situations

Property Developer

This classification is used for a business organisation whose business activity is the development of property, by purchase or purchase and refurbishment or construction, for commercial profit by sale or lease. The concern here is with those developments which consist of new construction or purchase and refurbishment of an existing property, which is then sold or leased. The use of each of the various methods for these situations is considered in turn.

(1) Comparable sale value method
This would be the most meaningful method if the project was intended for sale by the developer – for example housing, commercial offices or industrial buildings. The value ascertained by this method would perfectly reflect the developer's intended, realised aims for the project.
(2) Current capital value method
This would be appropriate if the project was intended for sale, in that it is a commonly used method for determining a sale value of certain types of property, particularly commercial offices. Its accuracy for this purpose depends on the efficiency of the sale market in reflecting the level of rate of return on such property.
    The method would be most meaningful if the developer's intended use was the retention of the freehold interest and the sale of leases in the property. The method was derived and developed from such utilisations and its formal conventions are accepted as the basis of value of such developments.
(3) Capitalised income method
This method would be inapplicable if the project was intended for sale. There would be no income to capitalise, other than the prospective sale price.

It would be theoretically appropriate if the project was intended to be retained on a freehold ownership with the generation of income by the granting of leases in the property. However, application of this method would present practical difficulties if the building had a long life cycle (more than ten years) and the intention was the long-term retention of the freehold in the property. The sufficiently precise prediction of rent incomes over a term in excess of ten years would not be possible for the future cash-flow profile required by this method. If the intended pattern of freehold ownership and leasing was short term, for example, industrial units with short life cycles, the capitalisation of the net rent income would be a meaningful method if linked to a risk analysis or identification technique, which is considered in Chapter 7.

(4) Target value method

This method would be inappropriate to a property developer whose aims for a project will be, by definition, identifiable income generation or sale.

Business Organisation

This description is intended to cover profit-making organisations – that is, companies, partnerships or sole traders, whose activities are undertaken for the purpose of making financial profit for shareholders, partners or the owner.

Property developers described above come within this definition but their activities, consisting as they do solely of property development, give their development projects distinct characteristics with regard to the appropriateness of methods of determination of value and for this reason are considered separately.

Two distinct types of development by business organisations can be identified that affect the choice of method, and these are now each considered in turn.

(a) *Development for the purpose of generating an identifiable income*

This describes those projects the purpose of which is to produce an identifiable and quantifiable income in the form of revenue or a saving on cost. Examples are the development by a manufacturing organisation of a production unit which is intended to result in an increased or new income flow from the product, and the development by a retail organisation of a new sales outlet facility.

The application of each of the methods of determining a project value in these situations is now considered.

(1) Comparable sale value method

This method would be appropriate in the sense that it produces a potentially realisable value for the project as an asset. However the following drawbacks to its use in this situation disqualify it as an ideally meaningful method.

The specialised nature of most projects that come within this classification would make it unlikely that there exists the identifiable and recorded market that is essential to obtain a reliable sale market value from a suitable comparable. Retail outlets are an exception to this.

The method fails to relate the cost of the project to its specific aim, that is, the generation of an identifiable income, which represents its real value. The costs of the project would only be meaningful in the contingency of the developer selling the project.

(2) Current capital value method

This method would be appropriate in the same sense as that of sale value in that it values an asset. It is subject to the same fundamental drawbacks of that method in that it does not relate cost to the project's purpose, that is, specific income generation over a defined life cycle, for it accounts only for a current income.

(3) Capitalised income value method

This is the most appropriate method. It relates the project costs closely to the aims of the project. A qualification would be that the income generation intended by the project must be sufficiently identifiable and quantifiable over a defined life cycle to facilitate the production of the required cash-flow schedule with realistic precision.

(4) Target value method

This method would be inappropriate as it would be unnecessary for a project whose intended income was identifiable.

(b) *Development for general operating purposes*

This description is intended to cover those projects which provide an operational facility for the developer's business activity but to which an identifiable, quantifiable income generation or cost-saving characteristic cannot be apportioned. Examples are administrative facilities, offices, storage buildings or staff welfare buildings.

In some of these examples, an income generation characteristic can be identified and quantified as the saving that accrues to the developer in the form of a cost that is no longer incurred by the removal of the need to pay for the facility which the project provides for. The development by a business organisation of its own office facilities rather than renting them would be a good example of this. Such income-saving projects are effectively income-generating projects as considered above. This section is concerned with projects for which, because of their developer-specific nature, no income can be identified and quantified, even in the form of a produced saving. The nature of the income-producing activities of many business organisations means that a large proportion of these organisations' built assets comes within this classification.

The application of each of the methods of determining the value of projects of this type is now considered.

(1) Comparable sale value method
This method is appropriate as a method of providing a value for an asset that would be realisable on sale. This does not fully reflect the value of the project in terms of its intended use. However, this is less of a defect in the method for this type of project than it is for the identifiable income-generating projects covered earlier, because the sale value may represent that which is closest to the project's only identifiable value to the developer. However, the specialised nature of such projects would mean the likely unavailability of comparables to produce a market sale value.

(2) Current capital value method
This method is most appropriate for those projects in this category that possess a theoretical, ascertainable income-generating potential. The best example of this type of project is an office facility. As stated previously, the current capital value is the conventionally accepted method of ascertaining a value for office buildings and would thus be an acceptable method of deriving a project value for a business organisation's proposed office building, even where the organisation intended the project for its own use rather than direct income generation.

Other types of building project for which current capital value is an appropriate method are warehouse buildings, which commonly come within this category of project for which no direct income to the developer can be identified and quantified, but for which there exists a sufficiently recorded rental market to enable yields to be ascertained, such yields then being available to calculate a current capital value.

(3) Capitalised income method
This method would be impossible as, by definition, there is no income to capitalise.

(4) Target value method
This method is appropriate and probably in most developments of this specialist nature the most appropriate. It requires a detailed performance analysis of the needs of the facility to be provided, and comparison of these with a relevant provision. Careful adjustment of the target set from the chosen similar provisions should be made, based on the relative performance of the project and the chosen comparable provision.

An additional consideration which should be taken into account when this method is used by a business organisation is the organisation's overall budget for the general provision of the facility of which the project forms part. For example, an organisation's overall budget for staff welfare provision would be a significant factor in its determination of the value of a project that consisted of the development of such a provision.

Non-business Organisation

Organisations within this classification are those whose ultimate aim is not the making of financial profit but whose reason for their activity is the meeting of an individual or group need or fulfilment of a charitable or statutory purpose. This would include:

Central and local government
Charitable organisations
Private, social organisations or clubs
Housing associations
Religious bodies

Some projects of such organisations may be undertaken with the intention of funding or part funding the project from income that is generated by the project itself, as opposed to being funded from the organisation's general resources. These two characteristics of funding from project income or from general funds have a significant effect on the appropriateness of the method of ascertaining a project value, therefore the two situations have been separately classified.

In practice, some projects of such organisations may consist of funding from both elements, that is, income and general resources. In these situations, a combination of the valuation methods described should be used, based on the principles subsequently explained for the two distinct funding situations.

Another common feature of development projects by such organisations is the provision to the developer of a grant or donation from another body to fund the project. This has no effect on the method or calculation of project value. The grant or donation should be presented in the development budget as a negative cost.

(a) *Projects financed by income generated by the project*
(1) Comparable sale value method
This method is appropriate in the sense that it values an asset. But it is subject to the defects identified above for its use in respect of developments by business organisations, that is, the likely lack of comparable

property and the non-relationship of its amount with the developer's intended utilisation.

(2) Current capital value method

This method is most likely to be inapplicable for these projects in that they are unlikely to have any profit-earning potential, as opposed to mere income generation, from which to provide a yield for the derivation of capital value. If, however, the nature of the project did possess some profit potential, then the method could be theoretically used to value the building as an asset. This would not, however, closely relate to the developer's intended use of the project.

(3) Capitalised income method

This is the most appropriate method, representing as it does the developer's intentions for the funding of the project by the raising of income. This would be subject to the method's requirements of a sufficiently precise identification of the project's future net income flows being ascertainable to convert to a present value.

The discount rate used for this method in these situations should be either the interest rate being earned by the developer on funds held, or the borrowing rate being charged against the developer on the amounts lent to finance the project. Which of these is used will depend on the developer's particular circumstances. This contrasts with the use of this method by business organisations, in which the discount rate used will be, as explained previously, the rate of return required or expected by the developer.

(4) Target value method

This method is inapplicable for projects in which the significant financing feature is the income generated by the project.

(b) *Projects financed from general funds*

(1) Comparable sale value method and (2) Current capital value method

The appropriateness of these methods would be as described above for projects to be financed by income generation.

(3) Capitalised income method

This method would be inapplicable as there is, by definition no income relevant to the project.

(4) Target value method

This method would be the most appropriate method for projects in this situation. The method should be applied as described earlier for business organisations, that is, with a performance analysis and appropriate adjustment between the project and a comparable provision.

An additional consideration is the organisation's available resources for the project.

4.4 SUMMARY OF USE OF METHODS OF CALCULATING PROJECT VALUE

Table 4.2 attempts to summarise the appropriateness of the different methods of project valuation for the defined development situations.

The development situations are identified in the table with the following references:

1(a) Property developer; project for sale.
1(b) Property developer; project for rent.
2(a) Business organisation; project with identifiable and quantifiable income.
2(b) Business organisation; project for operational purposes.
3(a) Non-business organisation; project financed by income from the project.
3(b) Non-business organisation; project financed from general funds.

The quantified level of the appropriateness of the method for each situation is as follows:

1. Nil
2. Low
3. Limited
4. Qualified
5. High

Table 4.2 Appropriateness of use of project valuation methods

Type of Project	Comparable Sale Value	Current Capital Value	Capitalised Income Value	Target Value
1 (a)	5	3	1	1
1 (b)	3	5	3	1
2 (a)	3	4	5	1
2 (b)	3	2	1	4
3 (a)	2	2	5	1
3 (b)	2	2	1	5

4.5 TAXATION: EFFECT ON PROJECT VALUE

Taxation is the financial levy by government, central or local, on individuals and organisations. Its imposition is governed by statute law, which determines the circumstances which give rise to the liability and the amount or rate of payment. These provisions are subject to frequent revision and, in the case of the amounts and rates of liability, regular, periodic adjustment.

The liability for and amount of taxation will affect the value of a building project in that its most common form is on the basis of an individual's or organisation's income, revenues or profit levels, the first two of these being elements which determine project value and the third being a factor in project feasibility. The precise effect of a developer's taxation liability on the value of a project can only be calculated with reference to the current, applicable legislative provisions and the particular income and revenue circumstances of the developer. The following is an outline of the taxation provisions currently relevant to building project development and an explanation of how these will affect project value.

(1) Income Tax and Corporation Tax

Income tax is a tax on the income of an individual. Corporation tax is a tax on the profits of a registered company. In the context of considering the value of an individual or company developer's project, their effects are the same.

If net income, derived from rent, sale or other form of income, is used as the basis of determination of project value, then any applicable tax, in the form of profit tax or income tax, must be allowed for in the calculation. However, it may not be possible to identify the particular tax liability of an individual project as this may be impossible to separate from the developer's overall liability. In this situation, the subsequent feasibility calculation, which usually consists of an appraisal of profit level (see Chapter 6), will have to be carried out while taking full account of any such overall liability. Similarly this will also be required if the project value was not ascertained on the basis of income.

(2) Capital Gains Tax

An individual or a company is liable for taxation on the financial gain made by the disposal of an interest in property. The gain consists, broadly, of the sale proceeds less the disposal and, index linked, acquisition costs. There are partial exemptions in the amount of the gain for individuals and complete exemptions in liability for owner occupiers and charities.

This tax will thus affect a project value determined on the basis of an intended sale. Its amount is the same as income or corporation tax, and it can be dealt with in the budget on the same basis as those taxes.

(3) Value Added Tax (VAT)

This tax takes the form of a charge made by a supplier against a receiver of goods or services. The charge is the specified percentage addition to the value paid for the goods or services. The charge must be made by the supplier when the goods or services are within the definition of a 'taxable supply' and are supplied in the course of business. The supplier pays in taxation the amount charged less amounts paid by himself to his suppliers. Thus the tax received by the government consists of a percentage levy on the net value added to goods or services by their supplier.

Goods or services (the 'taxable supply') may be liable for the standard rate charge (currently 17.5%) or zero rated or exempt. If the supplies are zero rated, the supplier is still entitled to recover the input tax he has paid on his own purchases, but input tax cannot be recovered on exempt supplies.

The relevance of VAT to value calculations in development budgets is in its effect on the net amount of any income that is used to determine project value. For example, the cost of building maintenance and running expenses, etc., and the gain of income, for example in the form of rent or operating revenue, may be taxable supplies and thus liable for charge. Thus these costs and incomes should include any applicable VAT charges in the calculation of their net amount for use in determination of project value.

(4) Local Taxation

The method of levying taxation by local, that is, county, borough, district, town and parish authorities, has been subject to, and is still undergoing, fundamental changes. Rates were replaced by the Community Charge in 1991 (in England and Wales), which was replaced by the Council Tax in 1993.

A local taxation based on property value, as was the situation with Rates and, for businesses only, under the Community Charge and, partially, under the Council Tax, affects the income derived from a property. Therefore, if the project value is to be determined by the project's net income, the tax can be accounted for by an adjustment of this income. Otherwise, the tax will affect the general financial position of the developer and should be considered at the project's financial feasibility stage.

4.6 FURTHER READING

Baum A. and Mackmin D., *The Income Approach to Property Valuation*, 2nd edn, Chapters 3 and 4. Routledge, 1989.

Britton W., Conellan O.P. and Crofts M.K., *The Cost Approach to Valuation*. RICS Research Report, 1992.

Britton W., Davies K. and Johnson T., *Modern Methods of Valuation*, 8th edn, Chapters 2–7. Estates Gazette, 1989.

Darlow C. (Ed.), *Valuation and Development Appraisal*, 2nd edn, Chapter 3. Estates Gazette, 1988.

Isaac D. and Steley T., *Property Valuation Techniques*, Chapters 1–3. The Macmillan Press, 1991.

Marshal P.J.L. and Yates A., *'Development appraisal'*, in *Quantity Surveying Techniques: New Directions* (Ed. Brandon P.S.). BSP, 1988.

Yates A. and Gilbert B., *Appraisal of Capital Investment in Property*. Surveyors Publications, 1991.

5 Project Cost

5.1 COST ITEMS

The project cost consists of the total of the items of direct expenditure incurred by the developer in the process of procuring the completed project in the form for which the project value was calculated.

Indirect costs may be incurred in this process. For example, general administrative expenses or taxation of the developer's organisation. Such costs are not considered in the analysis in this chapter. The accounting for such indirect costs, when they are applicable, is most effectively dealt with in the process of determination of project feasibility which is examined in Chapter 6.

The direct costs incurred in a project will be determined by the circumstances and requirements of that project. They can be classified as follows:

(1) Land acquisition
(2) Relocation
(3) Construction
(4) Commissioning
(5) Finance
(6) Taxation

The project's development budget prepared at the inception stage requires the identification of project, direct costs and the forecasting of their amount. Their forecast total will represent the developer's debit side of the budget, which will be balanced against the project's value (Chapter 4) in order to determine project feasibility (Chapter 6).

In the following sections, the classified possible cost items will be described and considered particularly in terms of the methods of forecasting or budgeting for their likely amount.

5.1.1   Land Acquisition Costs

These consist of the price paid by the developer for the land plus ancillary costs consisting of selling agent's fees, legal conveyancing costs and stamp duty.

The price that a developer will have to pay for a suitable property interest in land that is appropriate for the project purposes can be forecast on the basis of current market sale prices for land of a similar category.

In some development situations, the land may have already been acquired at the inception stage. It is often the acquisition itself which has generated the commencement of the project. In this case, no forecast of cost is required but the budget will include the actually incurred cost. However, this inclusion of a cost for land already ac-quired does depend on the particular policy of the developer. The development of a project by a developer who has been the long-term owner of unutilised land might not have any meaningful land cost to that developer.

Another common development situation is one where the land cost is the variable element in the development budget and the budget is prepared for the purpose of determining its amount. This is a usual technique in projects undertaken by commercial property devel-opers. In this situation a development budget is prepared with the land cost as the residual variable. The budget then effectively produces the amount which the developer can pay for the acquisition of the land to produce a given rate of return on a given amount of non-land acquisi-tion costs. This amount is termed the land's development value in this context. The technique of using the development budget to determine the amount of one residual budget element will be referred to again in Chapter 6.

The ancillary land acquisition costs referred to above can be forecast on the basis of a percentage amount of the sale price for the land. Currently, 1% would be a sufficiently accurate amount.

The proceeds of a sale of property vacated as a consequence of the commissioning of the project can be represented as a negative cost against this item of land acquisition costs. Its amount can be forecast on the same basis as described above.

5.1.2   Relocation Costs

This category includes those costs incurred by the developer in moving his organisation, activity or operations consequent upon the commis-sioning of the new project. It would include such items as removal expenses, obtaining temporary premises and disruption expenses.

These are particular to the developer and his circumstances and can only be forecast on this basis.

5.1.3 Construction Costs

These include the costs of the following:

(1) Planning and building approval
(2) Site preparation and demolition
(3) Building
(4) Design
(5) Project management

The first of these, the obtaining of planning and building approval from the relevant local government body, consists of fees charged by that authority. The fees chargeable are fixed by the authority and simply forecast on this basis.

Site preparation and demolition, if not undertaken as part of the construction operations, consists of the charges made for the work by a specialist contractor. These charges are best forecast by obtaining quotations from these specialists, or by reference to past, similar activities.

The third classified item, building cost, is usually the largest single cost in the project and the most significant determinant of project feasibility. A detailed analysis of building cost and the techniques for forecasting it for the development budget are made in sections 5.2 and 5.3.

Design costs and project management costs consist of the fees paid to the parties who undertake these functions for the developer. Alternatively, if they are carried out by direct employees of the developer, they consist of salaries and wages.

If the costs are in the form of salaries and wages then they represent an indirect cost of the project, as described previously, particularly if the developer has a continuing, multi-project programme of development. In this situation the cost of salaries and wages for design and project management services are best considered as an indirect cost or an overhead cost which will be accounted for in the feasibility appraisal of the project (Chapter 6).

If the costs are fees to other parties, their amount consists of the sum agreed in the contract made between the developer and the design and/or management parties. The amount of these fees is closely related to the amount of the building cost and the project management system used for the project. They can be effectively forecast as a percentage value of the building cost. In 1993, 12% would have been an accurate allowance. However, the demise of mandatory professional fee scales, the introduction of compulsory competitive tendering by government authorities for professional services and the greater use of non-traditional procurement methods will make this a more indefinite cost item in the future and one worthy of more detailed consideration, analysis and cost management attention.

5.1.4 Commissioning Costs

This denotes those costs that are incurred after the completion of the construction work, which are required to prepare the project for the developer's intended purpose.

For projects intended for sale, this category could include costs of marketing and selling agent's costs. The first of these can be forecast on the basis of a decision by the developer on the marketing require-ments of the project made from past experience. Selling agent's fees are usually based on a percentage of the sale price. The sale price will have been forecast in the value calculation in the budget and can thus be used to forecast the selling agent's fee on this percentage basis. Currently, 2% is a commonly charged fee.

When the project is intended for the developer's use, commission-ing costs will usually not be applicable. The user costs of the building, or their equivalent, generally will have been accounted for in the value calculation in the budget (see Chapter 4). An exception to this will be if the value was determined on a target value basis. If this is the case, unless the target value made allowance for user costs, which is difficult and distorts the performance determined target analysis, the devel-oper should make separate budgetary allowance for costs in use (maintenance, repairs, services and allied activities) of the building. Developers for whom target value is the most meaningful value ascer-tainment method are usually of the type (government, private, non-profit-making organisations) who would be accustomed to this budgetary arrangement.

5.1.5 Finance Costs

These are the costs incurred by the expenditure of capital in meeting the other cost items of the project. They consist either of interest charged on amounts borrowed to meet the capital expenditure or the interest that is lost by the developer in using capital reserves for the expenditure.

In the former case, the cost will be an actual, direct, project expendi-ture, based on a charged rate of interest, and must therefore be budgeted as a cost.

In the latter case, it will be an opportunity cost in the sense that the developer has lost a return on the capital expended and thus the cost will be based on an interest rate that represents the developer's required or expected rate of return or yield. However, the developer, if a profit-making organisation, will obtain a return on the capital expended in the form of the return derived from the project itself. This return from the project can be accounted for in the development budget in the feasibility calculation. However, this depends on the method used for the calculation. If the developer has used capital reserves for the project expenditure and the return on the project is accounted for in the feasibility calculation, then no finance costs need be accounted for in the cost section of the budget. This point will be returned to in Chapter 6, which considers methods of determining project feasibility in detail.

If project finance is a required cost item in the budget, its amount will be determined by the rate of interest and the period of the borrowing. The latter will be determined by the time profile of the project expenditure which will be determined by the project's programme and the resulting cash flow. The method of ascertaining finance costs on the basis of the developer's cash flow is covered in detail in Chapter 6.

In many development situations, the project programme may not be available or even forecastable at the stage when the development budget is required. Therefore, finance charges cannot be precisely forecast. However, there are rule-of-thumb techniques which are adequate for preliminary budgets.

One such method is to assume that project expenditure will be incurred at an even distribution over the project expenditure period, which can be estimated. Then the forecast interest rate can be applied to the total project expenditure for half of the estimated period. Thus:

Project expenditure	= £750 000
Project expenditure period	= 2 years
Short-term borrowing interest rate	= 15%
Finance cost	= 15% on 750 000 for 1 year
	= £112 500

The precise method of allowing for finance costs by preparing a cash-flow schedule and allowing for finance in the form of a rate of return on expenditure of capital reserves will be covered in detail in Chapter 6.

5.1.6   Taxation

Taxation is not usually a separate item of cost in the budget but may affect the amounts included for the other cost items given previously, in that certain forms of tax or tax allowance are applicable to these other items. Taxation items that affect building project budgets were identified in Chapter 4, section 4.5. Two of these items which will directly affect the amount of project costs are considered in the following sections.

Value Added Tax (VAT)

If a cost item in the budget is a taxable supply and not exempt or zero rated, the applicable standard rate must be added to the amount of the cost included in the budget. Detailed reference must be made to current legislation. All of the costs identified here are currently subject to standard rate tax, with the exception of finance charges and certain specialist types of building work.

Tax Allowance for Interest Charges

Interest payments made on loans for use in business are allowable against payments of income tax by individuals and corporation tax by companies. Therefore, if finance has been budgeted as a separate cost (see section 5.1.5), and the tax allowance which the intended loan may attract is sufficiently identifiable in the developer's finances, it can be adjusted in the budgeted amount. If these conditions do not apply, then the developer's overall tax burden should be considered, along with other indirect, project costs, against the calculation of project feasibility (Chapter 6).

5.2   ANALYSIS OF BUILDING COST

5.2.1   Introduction

Building cost, as analysed in this section, means the cost to the developer of procuring the construction work required by the project and the service of the management of the site operations that constitute this work.

In most development projects this cost is the largest single cost and, usually, the determinant of the amount of other costs, that is, design and project management costs. Together with land acquisition cost, building cost is the most significant factor in the determination of project financial feasibility. Land cost is largely determined by the general economic condition of the land market and thus, unlike building cost, is not susceptible to management cost control. Building cost, although marginally subject to factors external to the project, is a cost which is largely determined by the project requirements and is capable of close management control and manipulation. Once land cost has been determined, which usually occurs at an early stage of the project, building cost is the only significant cost variable. Therefore its effective cost management is essential for the achievement of the project's aims.

The different methods of procuring the building work required for a project were described in Chapter 3. The procurement method used will determine the exact form in which the developer incurs the cost, as it will determine the contractual arrangements made between the developer and the parties who provide the services.

For simplicity, in this section it will be assumed that the developer's building cost for building work and management of the building operations consists of the price of one party, that is, a general building contractor, who will carry out and manage the building operations. In fact, this would be the situation only under a traditional procurement system, but does not affect the explanation of the principles in their effects on the total building cost. Using alternative procurement systems, for example, construction management, the costs will be made up of the prices of many parties. The term price is used here to encompass all these prices.

The analysis is based on the following summarising formulae:

Developer's building cost = Builder's price

Builder's price   = Builder's resource costs

+

Adjustment for profit and risk

Builder's resource costs and the builder's price which results from the adjustment of resource costs for profit and risk are considered in turn in the following sections. The effect of market conditions on building costs will be considered in more detail later.

5.2.2 Builder's Resource Costs

The resources required by a builder for the execution of the building works of a project can be classified as follows:

(1) Labour
(2) Material
(3) Plant: machinery, equipment, plant, tools, etc.
(4) Site facilities; labour welfare, power, services, etc.

(5) Managerial
(6) Financial
(7) Organisation, general facilities

The cost to the builder of these resources takes the form of wages, salaries, hire charges, interest payments, suppliers' and sub-contractors' prices, rent and taxes.

The complexity and diversity of the form and content of a builder's resource costs for a particular building project give rise to the need for a model of analysis which relates these costs to the factors of the project which have an identifiable effect on the resource requirements. The factors which have this effect on the resource requirements of a project are:

(1) Quantity of work items
(2) Quantity of work
(3) Construction method requirements
(4) Construction period

Each of these factors are now considered.

(1) Quantity determined resource costs
One model which goes a considerable way to providing a meaningful indication of building resource costs is the analysis of building projects into quantities of finished work or quantities of work items. The use of quantities of work items based on the finished building is a traditional and still commonly used technique in the UK construction industry. It is used as the basis of obtaining prices for building work, building cost accounting, building cost forecasting and, with reservations, operational planning.

The method consists of breaking down the building project, in its completed design form, into geometrical quantities of work items for which the resource requirements for a unit quantity of the item can be quantified and costed.

The usual application of this technique consists of first establishing operational sections of building work based on the organisational structure of the building industry. One formally used system for this which is commonly used is that of the *Standard Method of Measurement of Building Work*, 7th edition (SMM7). Appendix A to this chapter gives the operational sections of a building as identified in this document.

Within this initial division of work into operational work sections, work items are identified. Unit quantities of these items, as required by the project are measured. SMM7 provides rules for the identification of work items and the form and content of the their measurement.

For quantities of work items in the finished project to be meaningful as a representation of the required resources, the items measured must be such as to facilitate the calculation of the resource costs of carrying out a single unit quantity of the item in the form of a rate for the item. This rate for the resource cost of the unit, when applied to the quantity of the item, produces the total cost of that item in the building. The totality of the cost of all the building's work items produces the total cost of the building.

Appendix B to this chapter shows examples of quantified and costed work items. Appendix C to this chapter shows the calculation of a rate of cost for one of the work items.

The effectiveness of this quantities model depends on the existence of a relationship in amount between the quantity of finished work items and the resource requirements of a building. Such a relationship clearly exists in regard to the resource requirement of materials, except with respect to the material quality, but less clearly so in regard to labour and not very clearly at all with respect to the other builder's resource cost items identified previously. The level of requirement for plant, site facilities, management, finance and the firm's general facilities is affected little, if at all, by the quantities of measured work items in the finished building. Factors other than quantities will determine the requirement for these resources.

(2) Quality determined resource costs

The quality of the building will affect the level of cost of material resources, labour resources and management supervision.

The first two of these can be adequately accounted for in the quantity model already described. Calculated unit rates can include material prices, which reflect their quality. They will also include labour requirements for defined items of work. These labour requirements, expressed in the rates in the form of labour outputs, can properly reflect the standard of workmanship necessary for the specified quality.

Management supervision cannot be expressed in any meaningful way in the unit rate for a quantity of work as it is not affected directly by the quantity of work.

(3) Method determined resource costs

Particular forms of building, with regard to such features as height and site conditions, will require particular methods for the construction operations necessary to construct the building. These methods will determine the nature and type and thus the cost of the plant and equipment required. They will also have an effect on labour outputs.

The necessary construction method of the project will thus determine the level of cost of plant resources and to a certain extent labour resources.

Costs of plant cannot be incorporated into a quantity based model of costs as few plant items can be related to narrowly defined work items. Almost all large plant items will be facilities utilised for a multiplicity of work items and thus cannot be reflected in unit rates for particular items. Plant costs are a reflection of the builder's cost of acquisition or hire of the item, the length of time it is required for the project and its output in operation. An example of the analysis of such a cost, usually referred to as a project overhead cost, is given in Appendix D to this chapter.

The effects on labour resources caused by the construction method can be allowed for in the quantity based method by adjustment of the labour output in the unit rate calculation.

(4) Construction period determined resource requirements

The time period of the construction work will largely determine the level of resource requirements of site facilities, management and finance. None of these resource costs can be represented in a model of quantities of work items. They must be costed on the basis of the rate of cost of their provision and the total period of their requirement.

However, there is a relationship between the overall quantity of work items required by a project and the project's time period; for the construction period will be significantly affected by the overall quantity of work, with the construction method and availability and productivity of labour being significant adjusting factors.

Non-project-related Resource Costs

The resource costs of a builder will include the cost of maintaining the organisation of the firm. This will consist, for example, of general office, administrative and managerial costs. These general organisation costs are usually referred to as *general overhead costs*.

Overhead costs of this kind are unrelated to the builder's operations in the construction of any particular project. But the firm will need to recover them in the prices it charges for its work. It will usually do this by a general, additional percentage, calculated on the basis of the relationship between past overhead costs and past project, resource costs. Thus the total for the resource cost of general overheads will be determined by the absolute cost of all other resources.

Summary of Builder's Resource Cost Factors

Table 5.1 summarises the points made in this section by approximately quantifying the relationship between the resources costs of a builder for a project and the characteristics of the project that affect the level of these costs.

The quantified level of the affect of the factors on resource costs is represented in Table 5.1 as follows:

Level of effect
1. Nil
2. Low
3. Limited
4. Qualified
5. Close

Table 5.1   Effects of factors on resource costs

Resource Cost	Cost Factor			
	1. Quantity	2. Quality	3. Method	4. Time
1. Labour	5	3	2	1
2. Material	5	4	1	1
3. Plant	3	1	5	3
4. Facilities	3	1	2	5
5. Management	3	4	2	5
6. Finance	2	2	2	5
7. Organisation	1	1	1	1

5.2.3   Builder's Price

The developer's building cost consists of the builder's price expressed in the contract made for the work between the developer and the builder. This contract may be negotiated or, more usually, made on the basis of sealed, competitive bids invited from a number of builders. The builder's bid will be made on the basis of the ascertainment of the project's resource costs with an adjustment, usually referred to as mark-up, to account for profit and risk. The level of the adjusting mark-up is a significant factor in the developer's project cost. The factors which determine mark-up can be classified as, firstly, the builder's required profit level and, secondly, the existence and nature of cost risk for the builder in undertaking the building work. These factors are each now considered in turn.

(1) Builder's profit
The builder's required profit will be expressed as a percentage adjustment to the ascertained or estimated total resource costs of the

project. The level of this adjustment for profit will be determined by the builder's expectations, requirements and need or desire for the work. These will be governed by the condition of the market for building work. The relative level of demand by developers for building work and the availability or willingness of builders to undertake it will be reflected in the profit levels charged by builders. At times of high levels of development activity, a builder's level of profit will reflect his desire or need for work and will thus generally be higher than at times of low demand when his need will be greater. This economic mechanism operates in the usually employed procedure by developers of competitive tendering. It is observable and forecastable by reference to published data on tender levels in identifiable building markets.

The adjustment for profit need not necessarily be a positive amount. For the definition of profit as simply the difference between total resource costs and total price is not the only and not the most meaningful definition. A builder's profit can be represented by the determination of the net cash flow of cost and income over the length of the project. A project in which the builder's cost and price balanced or were negative could produce a rate of profit return if the income exceeded cost during sufficient time stages of the project as this would in discounted, present value terms represent a positive balance of income against cost. The topic of developer's cash flow is considered in detail in Chapter 6, and applies equally to the profit rate of return of a builder.

However, for the purpose of providing data on which to base the forecast of market trends and profit levels, it is most effective to consider profit levels as the percentage difference between tender, price levels and resource costs.

(2) Builder's cost risk

The builder's price will be based on the resource costs of the project as identified in section 5.2.2, where the complexity of these costs and the difficulty of their analysis was made clear. Because, under most types of contractual arrangement for building work, the builder is committed to the contractual price, which has been based on the forecast of these costs, there is a risk in the builder's desired profit outcome. This risk can be covered in the mark-up made against the costs in deriving the price.

The techniques for quantifying and accounting for risk in general situations are still being developed. This is covered in more detail in Chapter 7. It is particularly difficult to quantify the risk element in building prices. However it is possible to identify the classified elements of risk borne by builders in their contractual commitment to a price for building work. These consist of labour productivity risk, method risk, and material and labour price fluctuation risk.

The risk of estimated outputs of labour will be greater for projects involving work of an innovative or special nature. For standard, conventional projects, labour outputs can be estimated with some confidence and thus little risk.

The choice of work method and the consequent decision on the equipment and plant requirements for a project have considerable cost significance. Therefore the correctness or effectiveness of the builder's decision on these matters gives rise to cost risk. For innovative building forms or projects with the complexity of multi-storey construction or other such factors, these decisions and the resulting estimates of cost carry considerable cost risk.

Material and labour costs are subject to the economic fluctuation effects of the market. For a project with a long duration these could be considerable and difficult to forecast with any certainty. If the contractual arrangement is one where the price is fixed and invariable, the risk of material cost escalation is with the builder. The level of this risk is largely determined by the length of the construction period.

5.3 FORECAST OF BUILDER'S PRICE AT DEVELOPMENT BUDGET STAGE

5.3.1 Basis of Development Budget Building Cost Forecast

A forecast of a builder's price for a project will require, in principle, the estimate and financial quantification of the resource costs identified in section 5.2.2 plus an adjustment for the estimated mark-up that will be added to this total cost. As can be seen from the factors identified in section 5.2.2 as those which affect resource costs, that is, quantity, quality, method and time, these are such as will be ascertainable only when a significant level of design of the project has been undertaken. Only the building size, form, quality and specification will indicate the extent of these factors.

At the development budget stage, that is, the inception stage of the project, it is unlikely that any design other than the first outline will have been undertaken and, in most development situations, it is most likely that no design at all will have been done. Therefore, for a forecast at this stage, a basis is required other than the project characteristics of quantity, quality, method and time. What is required is a characteristic of the proposed project that is cost sensitive in that it will be the ultimate determinant of the factors already identified, which will be expressed eventually in the building design or construction operations. The characteristic that best serves this purpose is the building's *function*. The ultimate determinant of the cost of a building will be the purpose for which it is constructed. Therefore the prices of past building projects which have the same function and purpose as that of the proposed project can be effective as a basis for the forecast cost of a project which is, as yet, undesigned.

Using building function as the basis of cost requires, firstly, that the cost can be expressed in a form which can be related to other proposed projects and, secondly, that this form is ascertainable at the inception stage of the project, that is, when no design has been undertaken.

The first of these requirements can be met by the expression of the cost in terms of a cost per floor area (m^2). This depends on the existence of a direct, effective relationship between the building price and the building's floor area. Floor area is the main determinant of the amount of the quantities of work items, which are the largest, single determining cost factor (section 5.2.2), given that storey height, which is the other quantity determining factor is not, in conventional buildings of a similar function, a significant variable.

The second requirement is met in that even at the very first inception stage of a project, floor area will be capable of reliable forecasting or is even already definitely decided.

In summary, the basis of the most effective method of forecasting building price at the inception stage is the unit, floor area prices of projects of the same function. The detailed application of this technique is explained in the following section.

5.3.2 Building Price Forecast by Floor Area

The method can be expressed by the following formula:

Forecast Building Price = Gross Internal Floor Area (GIFA)

$\times$

Mean unit price per m^2 GIFA of past projects with same function

$\times$

Adjustment for market fluctuations

$\times$

Adjustment for project special circumstances

The individual elements of this formula are each considered below.

(1) Gross internal floor area (GIFA)
The costs per unit floor area of past projects used for the project

forecast must be based on the same definition of GIFA as that used for the project calculation. One commonly used, standard definition of this term is that of the Building Cost Information Service (BCIS), who provide extensive data on building project prices, classified according to building function and expressed in terms of unit price GIFA. This definition, in brief, is that GIFA is the area of floors, within the building's external walls measured over stairs, lifts and service openings.

The precise calculation of GIFA, on the basis of the BCIS definition, will not usually be possible at the development budget, inception stage. However an effective approximation can be made for most projects. The function of the building identified at the inception stage facilitates the estimation of a GIFA that will be sufficient for the forecast at this stage.

(2) Mean unit price per m² GIFA of past projects with same function

The principle of the requirement of this part of the forecast's calculation is to obtain a mean price of a statistically significant sample of prices per m² floor area of past building projects of the same function as that of the project. The prices used to obtain this mean price must be adjusted to a common time basis.

The technique for making the adjustment to a common time basis, and also, adjusting for the variable market conditions which affect the level of mark-up of the individual prices, is considered in the next section. This present section discusses the method of selection of past projects from which to derive the unadjusted mean price.

The aim in the selection of an appropriate number of past similar projects from which to obtain a mean price is to obtain an aggregate that encompasses the likely range of prices in which the project price is expected to fall (on the basis of expert analysis).

What constitutes an appropriate number of past projects in this context will depend on circumstances. If, for example, the project is one for a developer who has commissioned a similar previous project or projects for which price data is available then merely that single project or the few projects would be sufficient and probably best. The same would apply for a project which is to be designed by an individual, whose previous, similar projects' price data is available. These would be situations in which there was expert, direct knowledge of the price circumstances of past projects which have a close similarity in features, in addition to function, to the proposed project.

Where such expert, direct knowledge does not exist, then as many as possible appropriate, past projects' prices should be considered and included in the aggregation.

Consideration should be given to every project included in this aggregation to identify any reasons which might cause a project to be excluded. Such reasons would include any special circumstances that caused the project not to be of a representative price within the expected range. When a mean price (market adjusted) has been derived from such a process, all the individual projects included in the aggregation should be checked against the mean to identify any individual price (market adjusted) which varies significantly from the mean. Plus or minus 25% would be a significant variation from the mean in this context. Consideration should than be given to identifying any special circumstance which would merit the exclusion of these projects and the recalculation of the mean.

Special circumstances which apply to the project to be forecast and give rise to the need for its adjustment are considered below (section 5.2.4).

The price of projects which were built at too great a period before the expected date of the proposed project should be excluded from the aggregation. This is to ensure that the cost implications of new technological and architectural developments are included in the forecast and the effects of outdated techniques excluded. The appropriate time period for exclusion depends on the type of project and the occurrence of cost significant developments, but as a general rule, projects older than five years should not be included.

(3) Adjustment of price for market fluctuations

Adjustment is required for the fluctuations that affect the level of building prices by reason of the factors identified in section 5.2.3, that is, the effect of the relative levels of demand for and supply of building work. This requires the quantification of the relative difference between the price levels at the time of the execution of the project or projects used to derive a mean price and the forecast price level at the time of the proposed project's execution.

This quantification can be done from indices of building prices that are derived from collected samples of such prices. The most suitable example of such an index is the *Tender Price Index* published by the BCIS (see Appendix E to this chapter). This index shows the aggregate value of a sample of tender prices for each quarter period of each year, with forecast values for future years. The value relates to a base value at a stipulated year, 1985. The values allow the calculation of the percentage variation in aggregate tender price levels between required dates by application of the following formula:

Price variation % ($\pm$) = Difference in index values at *A* & *B*
between dates *A* and *B*

$\div$

Index value at *A*

$\times$

100

An example of the use of this formula is as follows. The percentage increase in price level at 1989, second quarter from 1986, first quarter, based on the BCIS 'All in Tender Price Index' (Appendix E to this chapter) is given by:

$$\text{\% increase 1989 (2Q) from 1986 (1Q)} = \frac{134 - 101}{101} \times 100$$

$$= \underline{32.7\%}$$

This example illustrates the calculation of the percentage *increase* in building prices over a given period. Over most periods since 1945, prices have increased. One notable exception to this is the period from the last quarter of 1989, when the level of building prices began to fall. The percentage *decrease* in such periods is calculated by the formula above, an example of which now follows. Calculation of the percentage decrease in price level at 1991, fourth quarter from 1989, second quarter based on the BCIS 'All in Tender Price Index' (Appendix E to this chapter) is given by:

$$\text{\% decrease 1991 (4Q) from 1989 (2Q)} = \frac{134 - 111}{134} \times 100$$

$$= \underline{17.2\%}$$

The above adjustment must be made to all prices included in the aggregation of the mean rate to convert them to the date of the proposed project. Data collections of prices usually include a conversion of all prices to a base date; for example, the BCIS 'Cost Analyses'. In this case it is simpler to calculate a mean rate at the base date prices and then convert this mean price to the project date.

(4) Adjustment for project special circumstances

The aim and principle of the price forecast derived by the method described in this section is to produce a forecast price which is an achievable target for the project cost management, within the limits of the risk attached to such a forecast, whatever the circumstances that may arise to affect the proposed project. For the method is intended for use at the very earliest stage of the project when, in theory, no circumstances are known. Thus it is inconsistent with this principle to make special adjustments to the figure derived from the above techniques. However, certain special circumstances may be identified, even at the inception stage, and when known they should, of course, be accounted for. Also, the price forecast should be monitored, reconciled and amended as the project proceeds and cost-affecting circumstances do become known.

Therefore, the following is the identification of possible special circumstances which would require an adjustment to the past project-derived, market-adjusted mean price:

(1) Design requirements
Circumstances can require that the designed building is uneconomic in form. Plan shape is a significant factor in determining quantities of cost-sensitive elements such as the external walls, therefore any indication that site size restrictions or planning restrictions will dictate the need for a building of uneconomic form makes necessary an allowance in the forecast price.

Similarly, if the site for the project has been acquired and cost-affecting properties on it have been identified, for example, poor bearing capacity, high groundwater level or site obstructions, which would affect the costs of the substructure element, an adjustment would be required in the forecast price.

(2) Lack of functional relationship
Some projects may be multi-functional and not easily fit into the patterns of data collections of prices for functionally classified buildings. In this situation, expert analysis of the mean price and judged adjustment is required.

(3) Special market conditions
The indices available for adjustment of prices for market conditions are, generally, related to the UK national building market with some special building type features separately identified and some regional variations. If building work of the proposed project cannot be obtained on this market basis then adjustment is required.

(4) Procurement method
The majority of buildings are procured using the traditional system described in Chapter 3 with selective, competitive tendering usually the method of obtaining the contract for the building work. Thus, the data collections of prices will be dominated by past projects procured on this common basis. If alternative procurement methods are contemplated for the project then consideration should be given to the need for adjustment. The level of availability of definite, empirical data on the effects of procurement methods on price is low, therefore expert judgement is required.

5.3.3 Other Methods of Forecasting Building Price

The floor area method described in section 5.3.2 is the most appropriate method of forecasting building cost for the development budget at the inception stage, when the amount of design undertaken is minimal or non-existent. There are two other techniques which rely on the availability of greater levels of design information. Although these methods are not usually possible at the inception stage, they have a significant role in the cost management of the project. They should be used to monitor the accuracy of the first cost forecast as more design information becomes available, so that amending action or reconciliation can take place. The two methods are now described.

(1) Elemental price forecast
This method involves the price forecasting of individual design elements of the building and then their totalling to represent the forecast building price.

Design elements are the functional parts of a building. They are functional parts which are required by all conventional buildings and for which an individual element price can be analysed and forecast on the basis of the quantity and required performance of the identifiable elemental function.

A list of the BCIS defined design elements is given in Appendix F to this chapter.

A formula for this method can be expressed simply as:

Forecast price = Σ Element prices

The basis of this method is that with information available on the performance requirement and quantity of an element, a price can be forecast for it by reference to the element's price in a past project where it had a similar performance requirement. The quantity factor in the element's price can be accounted for either by measurement of the element's quantity or by expressing the price on the basis of the floor area of the building. Some elements, for example, a heating installation, have no meaningfully quantifiable element in themselves but are effectively expressed in terms of their price per unit of floor area.

The elemental price from a past project will have to be adjusted for market conditions for use in the project price forecast. This can be done by the method described for adjustment of floor area forecasts in section 5.3.2(3).

This method of price forecasting has great merit and is an essential part of an effective cost management process. It can be carried out as soon as the required level of design information is available, which will be at completion of the outline design stage. It can then be used to monitor the accuracy of the original price forecast made at the inception stage and then used as the basis of the design cost plan, which is essential for cost control at detail design stage.

(2) Approximate quantity price forecast
This method involves the measurement of approximate quantities of

work items, as described in section 5.2.2, that are required for the proposed project and estimating current, market, unit prices for these items. The total price arrived at with additions for non-quantity-related builder's costs then produces a forecast cost for the project. The method can be summarised in the following formula:

Forecast price = Σ Quantities of work items × market unit rate prices + market prices for plant, site facilities, management, finance and overheads

This method requires for its use the virtual completion of the detail design stage. Although the quantities are described as approximate, they must be taken to the degree of accuracy that gives cost significance. This effectively requires a near complete design. Thus the method can only be carried out at the end stage of the total design process. At this time a forecast can be useful as a further check on the initial cost forecast and the cost plan.

The method's most useful application, however, is for forecasting of projects or for parts of projects, the nature of which makes them incapable of forecasting by the floor area or elemental methods described above. Such situations are considered in the following sections.

5.3.4   Price-forecasting for Alteration/Refurbishment Projects

Projects that do not consist of the construction of complete, new buildings are not appropriate for use in price forecasting techniques that are based on the price significance of floor area or functional elements. Alteration projects are unique, with their resource requirements being related to their particular features and not to any model that relates their price to previous projects. Their price per unit floor area cannot be meaningfully compared with the prices for other alteration projects, and they will not have the elemental functional requirements that are the basis of elemental forecasts.

Therefore, the only method of forecasting the price of an alteration or refurbishment project is by the approximate quantity method described above (section 5.3.3(2)). The defect of this method for inception-stage price forecasts, as stated previously, is that it requires an advanced detailed design. This is not applicable for alteration projects. However because contemplation of such a project necessarily implies that the developer has some existing building identified to be altered or refurbished, the identification of the building to be altered coupled with the developer's stated functional requirements for the project allow meaningful approximate quantities to be prepared. However there is considerable risk in forecasting such projects owing to the inevitable uncertainty in the nature of the work required and the doubt that this places on resource requirements. This should be borne in mind when budgeting for the cost of alteration work, and the risk accounting procedures described in Chapter 7 are particularly applicable.

5.3.5 Price-forecasting External Works

External works means the works required outside the external walls of the building. It includes such items as roads, paths, landscaping, boundary walls and fencing, and drainage and service connections. All projects have some level of external works requirement but the extent is highly variable and completely dependent on the circumstances of the project, particularly, the nature of the site and its location in relation to main services and surrounding buildings.

Thus the price of external works cannot be derived from past project prices based on the existence of a model relationship in price per unit floor area or functional element. The price of these items must be forecast on the basis of approximate quantities. As no design details will be available at inception stage for this process, this presents a problem.

The best solution is to make an allowance in the building price forecast to cover external works provision. As this provision will not closely relate to total project price, it is not completely appropriate to make this allowance on a percentage of the other building work forecast price. However, this basis, coupled with expert judgment, is the only method available. The percentage allowance made should be checked and adjusted as soon as approximate quantities can be calculated. This can be done when the site is identified, which is usually at an early stage and may even have been reached at inception, in which case an approximate quantity forecast can be included with the floor area forecast of the building.

5.4 FURTHER READING

BCIS, *Study of Average Building Prices: Histograms*. Building Cost Information Service, 1992.

BCIS, *Manual*, section A (Tender Price Indices) and section G (Detailed Cost Analyses). Building Cost Information Service (continually updated collection of data).

Brandon P.S. (Ed.), *Building Cost Techniques: New Directions*, Spon, 1988.

Brandon P.S. (Ed.), *Building Cost Modelling and Computers*. Spon, 1987.

Chrystal-Smith G. (Ed.) and Geddes S., *Estimating for Building and Civil Engineering Works*, 8th edn. Butterworth, 1985.

Darlow C. (Ed.), *Valuation and Development Appraisal*, 2nd edn, Chapter 5. Estates Gazette, 1988.

Ferry D.J. and Brandon P.S. *Cost Planning of Buildings*, 6th edn, BSP, 1990.

Lock D., *Project Management*, 4th edn, Chapter 3. Gower, 1988.

Marsh P.D.V., *The Art of Tendering*. Gower, 1987.

Pilcher R., *Project Cost Control in Construction*, Chapters 6 and 8. BSP, 1985.

Raftery J., *Models for Construction Costs and Price Forecasting. RICS Research Technical Paper No. 6*. RICS, 1991.

RICS/BEC, *Standard Method of Measurement of Building Work*, 7th edn (SMM7). RICS, 1988.

Seeley I.H., *Building Economics*. The Macmillan Press, 1983.

Skitmore M., *Early Stage Construction Price Forecasting: A Review of Performance*. Occasional Papers, RICS, 1991.

Skitmore M. and Patchell B., 'Developments in contract price forecasting and bidding techniques', in *Quantity Surveying Techniques: New Directions* (Ed. Brandon P.S.). BSP, 1988.

Tysoe B.A., *Construction Cost and Price Indices: Description and Use*. Spon, 1990.

APPENDIX A TO CHAPTER 5: OPERATIONAL BUILDING WORK SECTIONS

The following is from *Standard Method of Measurement of Building Works*, 7th edn, RICS/BEC.

(1) Demolition
(2) Groundwork
(3) Concrete
(4) Masonry
(5) Structural carcassing
(6) Cladding
(7) Waterproofing
(8) Linings and dry partitions
(9) Joinery
(10) Surface finishings
(11) Furniture and equipment
(12) Building fabric
(13) External works
(14) Disposal systems
(15) Piped supply systems
(16) Ventilation/air conditioning
(17) Electrical power and lighting
(18) Mechanical heating
(19) Communications
(20) Transport

APPENDIX B TO CHAPTER 5: QUANTIFIED WORK ITEMS

	Work Section MASONRY	Quantity	Unit	Unit Rate Resource Cost	Total £	
	BRICKWORK					
	Common bricks, BS 3921, solid ordinary quality; in sulphate resistant cement mortar (1:3); stretcher bond					
	Skins of hollow walls					
1.	half brick thick	60	m²	28.19	1 691	40
	Red Rustic Facing bricks; in sulphate resistant cement mortar (1:3); stretcher bond; bucket handle jointing as work proceeds.					
	Skins of hollow wall					
2.	half brick thick; facing and jointing one side	110	m²	95.76	10 533	60
	Engineering bricks Class B; in sulphate resistant cement mortar (1:3); in stretcher bond; bucket handle jointing as work proceeds.					
	Sills; bricks-on-edge; set slightly weathered, pointing top and one side					
3.	170 × 103; horizontal; raking cutting	10	m	10.43	104	30
4.	Ends	2	Nr	1.50	3	00
	Damp-proof course; BS 743; bitumen reference C; 150 laps					
	On horizontal surfaces					
5.	103 wide	20	m	6.75	135	00
	Damp-proof course; BS 734; slates 4 thick					
	On horizontal surfaces					
6.	over 225 wide; (0.49 m²)	1	Nr	5.75	5	75
		To collection		£	12 473	05

APPENDIX C TO CHAPTER 5: EXAMPLE OF UNIT RATE RESOURCE COST CALCULATION

Item Common bricks, BS 3921; solid ordinary quality:
in sulphate resistant cement mortar (1:3);
Stretcher bond
Skins of hollow wall
Half brick thick
Unit m^2

Material	£

1. Bricks: Common bricks delivered to site
   $= £75.00$ per thousand
   No of bricks per m^2 half brick thick $= 58$

   $\therefore £75.00 \times \dfrac{58}{1000} =$ **4.35**

2. Mortar: Mortar (1:3) mixed $= £60$ per m^3
   Mortar per m^2 half brick $= 0.03$ m^3 @ £60.00 $=$ **1.80**

   Labour

   Bricklayer All-in rate £10.50 per hour
   Labourer All-in rate   £8.50 per hour
   Total gang rate =   £19.00 per hour

   Gang output = 50 bricks per hour

   $\therefore 1\ m^2 = \dfrac{58}{50} \times £19.00$ **22.04**

   £28.19

APPENDIX D TO CHAPTER 5: EXAMPLE OF CALCULATION OF PROJECT OVERHEAD COST

MORTAR MIXER (Purchased)

Capital cost £6000.00
Years of productive use = 3
Total cost of investment at 10%:

Cost (Year 1)	6000.00
× Amount of £1 in 3 years at 10% =	1.3310
Capital cost =	£7986.00

Hourly cost
Estimated hourly use per year   2200 hrs

Hourly cost $\dfrac{£7986}{3 \times 2200}$ $=$ 1.21

Maintenance 10%   0.12
Fuel   0.09
Cost for project hour requirement   **£1.42**

APPENDIX E TO CHAPTER 5: BUILDING PRICE INDEX

The following is from the *BCIS Tender Price* indices published June 1992.
'All-in Tender Price Index' (Base 1985 mean = 100)

Quarter		Index	No of tender prices in sample
1984	i	94	37
	ii	96	29
	iii	95	41
	iv	96	68
1985	i	97	82
	ii	102	61
	iii	99	84
	iv	103	54
1986	i	101	77
	ii	102	78
	iii	103	70
	iv	105	79
1987	i	108	88
	ii	106	87
	iii	109	94
	iv	117	81
1988	i	119	95
	ii	122	71
	iii	128	109
	iv	128	86
1989	i	134	91
	ii	134	78
	iii	138	86
	iv	135	94
1990	i	135	94
	ii	131	72
	iii	126	80
	iv	122	72
1991	i	117	77
	ii	114	81
	iii	113	94
	iv	111	59
1992	i	113	15
	ii	113*	
	iii	114*	
	iv	114*	
1993	i	115*	
	ii	117*	
	iii	119*	
	iv	120*	
1994	i	122*	
	ii	124*	

* = Forecast figures.

APPENDIX F TO CHAPTER 5: DESIGN ELEMENTS

The following are elements as identified by the BCIS for their Standard Form of
Cost Analysis. Full definitions of the elements and methods of measurement
are contained in that form.

1.   Substructure
2A.   Frame
2B.   Upper floors
2C.   Roof
2D.   Stairs
2E.   External walls
2F.   Windows and external doors
2G.   Internal walls and partitions
2H.   Internal doors
3A.   Wall finishings
3B.   Floor finishings
3C.   Ceiling finishings
4A.   Fitting and furnishings
5A.   Sanitary appliances
5B.   Service equipment
5C.   Disposal installations
5D.   Water installations
5E.   Heat source
5F.   Space heating and air treatment
5H.   Electrical installations
5I.   Gas installations
5J.   Lift and conveyor installations
5K.   Protective installations
5L.   Communication installations
5M.   Special installations
5N.   Builder's work in connection with services
5O.   Builder's profit and attendance on services
6A.   Site works
6B.   Drainage
6C.   External services
6D.   Minor building work

6 Project Feasibility

6.1 INTRODUCTION

This chapter is concerned with the determination of the financial feasibility of the building project. This means the ascertainment of whether the project, in the form budgeted, meets the financial objectives or is within the financial, expenditure limits of the developer. This ascertainment depends on the relationship between the project's value (Chapter 4) and cost (Chapter 5). There are three main classifications of the methods for determination of the value and cost relationship, and these are described and analysed for their suitability in use in section 6.2 below

In the form in which the development budget has been presented in this book, the value and cost relationship is the variable factor which the budget was prepared to ascertain. That is, feasibility is determined on the basis of forecastable or realised items of cost and revenue. In many development situations this may not be the required purpose of the development budget. It may be that a particular cost or value item is the variable element, that is, the item the value of which requires to be ascertained for a given rate of return and for given costs.

An example of this situation would be that where the budget is prepared to ascertain the amount of cost that can be expended on land to produce a given value and cost relationship (see Chapter 5, section 5.1). Another would be the developer of social homes, that is, a housing association or local housing authority, for whom the critical variable to be ascertained in the budget would be rent that could be charged for the homes developed.

The principles of budget preparation in these residual variable situations is the same as these of budgets in the form presented in the foregoing chapters of this book as well as in this one.

6.2   METHODS OF DETERMINATION OF PROJECT FEASIBILITY

All the methods of ascertaining financial feasibility consist, in principle, of a comparison of project value and project cost. But there are
significant differences in the way the resulting comparison can be
analysed. It is this analysis which determines the classification of the
possible methods. These are as follows:

   (1) Balance of realised value and incurred cost
   (2) Balance of present value
   (3) Rate of return

Each of these methods is now considered.

6.2.1   Balance of Realised Value and Incurred Cost

This is the most straightforward and immediately comprehensible
method, involving as it does the calculation of the balance between the
project value, derived by whichever of the methods described in Chapter 4 is the most appropriate, and the total project cost, as defined in
Chapter 5. The balance is the result of the deduction of cost from
value.

Generally, a positive amount for this balance denotes financial feasibility and a negative one the opposite.

If the developer is a profit-making organisation, the amount of the
balance, when positive, can be classified as profit. However, indirect
project costs which have not been included in the budgeted project
costs, for example, general overheads and taxation (Chapter 5), will
have to be set against this. The balance, when classified as profit, is
most meaningfully represented as a percentage of the project value.
This facilitates the preference ranking of alternative projects, in
terms of their relative rate of profitability. The balance expressed as a
percentage of project cost, rather than value, can be considered as a
yield rate of return on capital expenditure investment.

In the situation where the developer is not a profit-making organisation, the existence of a positive balance between value and cost
denotes project feasibility and, if appropriate, the availability of additional funds to expend on the project.

6.2.2   Balance of Present Value

This method is the calculation of the balance between the amounts of
the equivalent present values of the project value and the project cost.
The present value (PV) of these amounts is the equivalent amount of
their actual amount, discounted to allow for the time of payment of the

cost and the time of the realisation of the project value. Chapter 2, section 2.4 considered the concept of present value in detail.

An unbudgeted element in method 1 (Balance of realised value and incurred cost), described in section 6.2.1, is the effect of the time profile of cost expenditure and realisation of the project value. All projects, other than the very smallest, will have a developer's expenditure profile spread over a period of time and the value will not be realised until it is complete. Thus, considering only incurred cost and realised value does not account for the costs or benefits that may arise from the later liability for a cost or realisation of a value. The amount of these time-related costs and benefits will be determined by the project programme which determines the project cash flow. The balance of present value method accounts for these costs and benefits by discounting the actual amounts to their equivalent present value.

The basis of the method is to calculate, firstly, the present value of project costs, secondly, the present value of the project value, and then balance these amounts on the basis described for the balance of actual cost and value described in section 6.2.1. That means a positive amount resulting from the deduction of cost (PV) from value (PV) denotes project feasibility, and the percentage rate of this amount against value (PV) or cost (PV) represents, respectively, profit or a rate of return on capital expenditure.

The techniques for calculation of the equivalent present values of project cost and value are each considered in the following sections.

A. *Calculation of Present Value of Project Cost*

The project costs (classified and listed in Chapter 5, section 5.1) need to be scheduled according to the precise time in the project programme that they will be incurred and paid. At the inception stage the project programme will not usually have been definitely determined and will need to be forecast. The process of identification and forecast of total project cost that necessarily will have taken place for the budget at this stage will facilitate this forecast of programme, although certain decisions on procurement method will need to be considered.

The forecast programming of the project costs clearly depends on the nature of the project but, in general, the most significant item of cost, building cost, will be the only cost that will be substantially spread over the duration of the project. The other costs will either be single point costs, for example, land acquisition, or costs that are determined by the building cost profile, for example, design costs. Thus forecast scheduling of the building cost is the critical item.

The typical developer's building cost profile is based on the payment to the builders, in stages, during the construction period. The amount of these payments is determined by the value of work executed in the relevant payment period and this, in turn, is based on the builder's resource costs for the work executed during the period. Thus, an effective method of forecasting the developer's building cost, payment profile is on the basis of the forecast resource utilisation for typical construction work.

There are certain, general features of the builder's resource utilisation profile in the construction of typical projects. In the initial period of sitework, resource use will be relatively slow, consisting as it does of preparation and site setting-up activity. During the middle period, resource use will be at its highest, with all operational work sections having an input to site activity. The final period will have a resource use rate equal to that of the initial period as individual operational work sections are completed and relatively less expensive finishing work sections complete the work. This typical model can be represented graphically: see Appendix A to this chapter. It produces an S-curve representing the initial and final low resource utilisation. This model is intuitively expert-derived, based on observation, but difficult to forecast in precise detail. However, the principle is a reliable one to use for the initial programming of project costs.

An adequate calculation would be based on the forecast that 10% of the building cost will be incurred during the initial one-fifth of the construction period, 80% of the cost during the middle three-fifths of the construction period, and 10% during the final one-fifth period.

Adjustment to this basis would be required in the following circumstances:

(1) Stage payments
The conventional contractual arrangements between a developer and a builder for interim payments to the builder are for the amounts of these payments to be determined by the value of the work executed in the relevant interim period. Any variation to this form of arrangement, such as the agreement of predetermined payments at agreed stages of construction, would require adjustment to the forecast profile. Such an arrangement would, in fact, make the cash flow forecast more certain. However, the risk it would give to the developer of incurring loss due to a builder's insolvency might weigh against this advantage.
(2) Non-typical building work
The building work for which the cost profile described above is typical new building work of a single faceted nature, that is, comprising the consequential execution of standard operational work sections, defined in Chapter 5, section 5.2.2(1). If the work is not of this type, for example, alteration and refurbishment work or repetitive work such as housing, then the pattern of payment will alter. For repetitive work,

the profile would usually become more uniform and evenly spread over the project.

(3) Retention of payment

Most building contracts provide that the amounts due for interim payment by the developer to the builder will be subject to the deduction of a percentage amount to cover defects and the risk of non-completion by the builder. This amount will usually be between 3% and 5%. The total amount retained will be released to the builder when the project is complete and all defects rectified, and one-half on practical completion. This will typically occur one year after project completion. This retention release payment must be programmed in the cash flow schedule and any significant variation to its amount in the contractual provision should be allowed for.

The time-scheduled total project costs are collected in the form of a cash flow schedule which gives the net costs for each period. The appropriate period for most development projects is an annual one, but this can be altered to monthly cash flow scheduling for projects of less than two years' programme duration or for projects which required a very detailed cash flow analysis. These annual (or monthly) payments are then discounted to a present value. The feasibility calculation in Appendix B to this chapter gives an example of the cash flow schedule and present value calculation for a defined project.

The choice of discount rate for this calculation should be made on the following basis:

(1) Developer's required rate of profit return

By reflecting this rate, the budget will have incorporated a profit on the development, and the resulting balance of cost against value must take this into account.

If this rate is used and the developer is using capital reserves to fund the project, then no opportunity cost for the lost return on capital expended is required in the budget costs.

(2) Interest rate

If the rate used is the cost of borrowing, reflecting the interest that the developer will pay on borrowed funds for the project then, once again, no such cost need be separately budgeted. However, this rate of discount will not account for the developer's required profit and the consideration of the balance of cost against value will need to take account of this.

(3) All in rate

A rate can be used to account for the cost of borrowing and the required rate of return. In this case no cost of borrowing nor opportunity cost need be included in the project cost. Also, the balance of cost and value should be judged on the basis that profit has been accounted for. However, there may be indirect costs of the developer's organisation to set against this balance.

B. *Calculation of Present Value of Project Value*

This calculation is simpler than that used to discount project costs, for a project value calculated by the four methods given in Chapter 4, section 4.2, will produce a single amount, thus no cash flow schedule is required. However, depending on the basis of the value calculation, the amount might have to be discounted, as the value must be on the same present value basis as that used for costs. Particular points with regard to this discounting requirement for each of the methods of determining a project value are now considered.

(1) Comparable sale value method
If the value was calculated on this basis, it will have been done, most effectively, as the *current* comparable sale value. This is effectively a present value and thus requires no discounting. If, however, the comparable sale value calculated is one forecast to be realised upon completion, then this amount will have to be discounted to a present value, that is, the same present value basis as that to which the costs have been discounted.

(2) Current capital value method
If this method was used to derive a value current at the present time, then no discounting for a meaningful comparison with the present value of costs is required. However, the value calculated may have been one current at the time of the project's completion, in which case it will require discounting to the present value basis used for discounting costs.

(3) Capitalised income method
The method consisted of discounting future incomes to a present value. However the technique for this involved the present value being a nominal Year 1, used to represent the year in which the revenues will start to accrue. This will not occur until the project is complete and operating to generate the income which was used to derive the value. Thus the capitalised income will have to be discounted to the same present value basis as that to which costs have been discounted, that is, the current year.

(4) Target value method
This value is one nominally applicable at the time of project completion. It is actually applicable at this time if it is based on comparable project costs which were adjusted for market factors to make them the equivalents for the project completion time. The value should, there-

fore, be discounted to the same present value basis of that of the project costs.

The discount rate used for the calculation of the present value of the project value, if required, should be chosen on the same basis as that used for discounting project costs (see section A above).

Summary of Balance of Present Value Method

(1) Prepare the time profile schedule of the total project costs.
(2) Discount costs to present value using a rate based on interest charges and/or the required rate of return, as appropriate.
(3) If appropriate, discount the project value to its present value using an appropriate rate, as for costs.
(4) Derive the balance of cost (PV) deducted from value (PV) for determination of feasibility.

Appendix B to this chapter illustrates the summarised method.

6.2.3 Rate of Return

This method determines feasibility on the basis of the rate (%) which discounts the future value of the project to the same amount as the present value of the project costs. The rate which is produced by this method constitutes a rate of profit return on the project in that it expresses the difference between cost and value as a rate percentage.

This method is a refinement of the balance of present value method, in that it equates value and cost to the same time adjusted level but, rather than requiring the selection of a rate to discount project value, it makes this the variable factor to be ascertained for the situation of cost and value being equal.

It requires, firstly, the calculation of the present value of costs which is carried out in the same way as described above, that is, the time scheduling of total project costs and the discounting of these to a present value. The rate used for this should be chosen on the same basis as that described for the balance of present value of value and cost method, that is, either the interest charge on borrowing or the opportunity cost of expenditure of reserves represented by a rate percentage. Secondly, the discount rate which converts the project value to equal the calculated present value of costs is calculated. This, of course, requires that the project value is a future cost.

The method can be summarised in the following formula:

Project rate of return   = The rate% which discounts the future value of the project to equal the present value of the project cost

The calculation of this rate is now illustrated using the project costs and values ascertained for the example given in Appendix B to this chapter, that is:

Project cost (PV)   = £3.415 million
Project value   = £4.77 million realisable in Year 5

The rate of return for this project is the rate percentage which discounts £4.77 million in five years time to £3.415 million. This rate can be calculated from the formula given for present value in Chapter 2, section 2.4.3, that is:

$$\text{PV of £1} = \frac{1}{(1 + i)^n}$$

where i = the rate of interest expressed as a decimal
        n = the total term in years.

Thus the discount rate or rate of return which discounts value to the same amount as the present value of costs in the above example can be calculated thus:

$$3.415 \text{ (PV of costs)} = 4.77 \text{ (Project Value)} \times \frac{1}{(1 + i)^n}$$

where n, the term, is 5 years and i, the rate of interest, is the rate of return to be found. Thus:

$$i = 0.0691$$
$$\text{Rate of return} = \underline{6.91\%}$$

Alternatively, the rate can be calculated using tables rather than the formula by ascertaining the discount factor and interpolating this from the table factors to find the appropriate rate for the given period. Thus:

Cost (PV) = Value (in Year 5) × Factor for PV of £1 in Year 5 at $X\%$
3.415   = 4.77 × Factor PV £1 in year 5 at $X\%$

$$\text{Factor} = \frac{3.415}{4.77}$$

$$= 0.71593$$

From the PV factors in the table for Year 5, the relevant rate percentage can be found. It can be found precisely by interpolating the factors in the table. In this case it produces a rate of return of 6.91%.

The rate derived by this method is effectively a rate of profit return. This is so provided that finance costs have been incorporated elsewhere in the budget, either as a cost item or in the chosen rate used to discount costs. It is also subject to consideration for indirect costs.

6.3   SUITABILITY AND USE OF METHODS OF DETERMINATION OF FEASIBILITY

The selected method of assessing financial feasibility depends on the nature of the developer and the circumstances of the project's cost incurrence and value realisation. In this context, the classifications of type of developer and possible utilisations of projects that were used to analyse the most meaningful method of ascertaining project value (Chapter 4, section 4.3) is not as significant as in that situation.

The main distinction in the methods is that between method (1), that is, the balance of actual cost and value, and both methods (2) and (3), which are both based on time discounted values.

Method 1, taking no account of the time value of expenditure and received income, is only meaningful for a developer who has no requirement for a rate of return on capital or who has no requirement to borrow money and incur an interest charge cost. It would also be appropriate for a project which had no time profile, that is, immediate cost and realisation of value.

Methods (2) and (3), the present value based methods, will be usually the most effective methods. There is little difference in principle between these methods. Their appropriateness is usually based on their techniques of calculation. The rate of return method is more suited to computer-programmed methods.

6.4   FURTHER READING

Britton W., Davies K. and Johnson T., *Modern Methods of Valuation*, 8th edn, Chapters 7 and 10. Estates Gazette, 1989.

Darlow C. (Ed.), *Valuation and Development Appraisal*, 2nd edn, Chapters 1 and 3. Estates Gazette, 1988.

Gilbert T. and Yates A., *Appraisal of Capital Investment in Property*. RICS, 1991.

Marshal P. and Yates A., 'Development appraisal', in *Quantity Surveying Techniques: New Directions* (Ed. Brandon P.S.). BSP, 1988.

Pilcher R., *Project Cost Control in Construction*, Chapter 3. BSP, 1985.

APPENDIX A TO CHAPTER 6: RESOURCE USE PROFILE FOR TYPICAL NEW BUILD CONSTRUCTION PROJECT

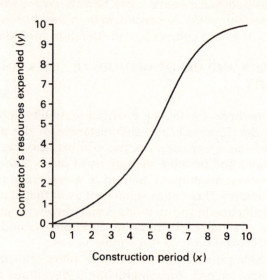

APPENDIX B TO CHAPTER 6: FEASIBILITY CALCULATION USING PRESENT VALUE METHOD

1. *Project Details*

Developer: Food retail company
Project: New supermarket

Project Value: £4.77 million, based on capitalisation of future net income generated by the project commencing from completion date

Programme: Total period   = 42 months
             Inception and design   = 12 months
             Construction period   = 30 months from completion of design

Costs: 1. Land acquisition £0.5 million to be paid in Year 1.
             2. Construction:
                1. Planning and building approval £1000 paid in Year 1.
                2. Building £3.1 million: traditional procurement. Usual monthly interim payment provision with 5% retention.
                3. Design and Management fees: 12% of building cost payable in equal instalments during total programme period.
             3. Funding: project to be financed from reserves. Required rate of return on capital investment = 6%.

2. Building Cost Cash Flow

		£ million
	Building total	3.100
less:	Retention at 5%	0.155 payable in Year 5

2.945 payable in 30 monthly instalments in Years 2, 3 and 4 (see below)

Building Cost Instalments:
First 1/5 period (months 1–6, Year 2)   = 10% of 2.945 = 0.2945 = 0.04908 per month
Middle 3/5 period (months 7–12, year 2
   and months 1–12, Year 3)   = 80% of 2.945 = 2.356 = 0.130889 per month
Final 1/5 period (months 1–6, Year 4)   = 10% of 2.945 = 0.2945 = 0.04908 per month
                                       Total   2.945

Year 2	= (6 × 0.04908)	+ (6 × 0.130889) =	1.0798
Year 3	= 12 × 0.130889	=	1.5707
Year 4	= 6 x 0.04908	=	0.2945
Year 5	= Retention 5%	=	0.1550
			3.1000

3. Total Cost: Cash Flow Schedule and Present Value

Year	Costs £ million						
	Land	Planning, etc.	Building	Design, etc. (12% of building cost)	Total	PV of £1 at 6%	Present Value
1	0.5	0.001		0.0744	0.5754	0.94340	0.5428
2			1.0798	0.0744	1.1542	0.89000	1.0272
3			1.5707	0.0744	1.6451	0.83962	1.3813
4			0.2945	0.0744	0.3689	0.79209	0.2922
5			0.1550	0.0744	0.2294	0.74726	0.1714
Total	0.5	0.001	3.1000	0.3720	3.973		3.4149

Present
Value = £3.415 million

4. Project Value: Present Value

	£ million
Project Value: realisable in Year 5 =	4.77
× PV of £1 at 6% in Year 5	0.74726
Present Value	= 3.5644 million

5. Feasibility

		£ million
PV Project Value	=	3.564
Less PV Project Cost	=	3.415
Net Balance	=	0.149

This balance represents a profit rate of 4.2% on project value and 4.4% on project costs, which is in addition to the 6% return allowed by the discount rate.

7 Project Risk: Analysis and Management

7.1 INTRODUCTION

The development budget represents a statement of the financial value and cost of the project, quantified so as to allow the determination of financial feasibility. Prepared, as it must be, at the earliest stage of the project's inception, its amounts will be based on, usually almost exclusively, forecasts – that is, informed guesses, estimates or expert predictions of future occurrences. The occurrences which have to be forecast will consist of prices for land and services, revenue from business activities, programme times and economic circumstances which influence these phenomena, such as interest rates and market inflation. The possibility of the eventuality of the forecast of such occurrences being precisely fulfilled ranges from highly unlikely to impossible. This high probability of the non-fulfilment of the precise forecast, budgeted amounts means that development projects have, for the developer, a degree of risk and uncertainty.

The terms 'risk' and 'uncertainty' are commonly used, in this context, to denote different qualities. *Risk* is the possibility of a forecast being not accurately fulfilled by the actual occurrence of the cost or receipt of revenue. *Uncertainty* is the possibility of the occurrence of an event which cannot be budgeted for and which would defeat the project's aims or for which no reliable basis for a forecast exists.

Most proposed building projects are such as to facilitate the identification of likely cost factors and generally these will be of a type which can be forecast, therefore uncertainty of the fundamental type defined above will not be commonly present, except for the natural opposition of events that accompanies all human endeavour. However, the nature of the forecasts which make up a typical development budget mean that projects are seldom, if ever, free of risk, in the sense of that term as defined above, that is, the possibility of a variation between the forecast amount and the actual project amount.

This being so, how can a development budget fulfil its primary function of providing the financial basis for the developer's decision on whether or not to undertake the project? A general answer to this question is the negative one that no projects would be undertaken if the absence of risk was a prerequisite. A more meaningful answer is that the development budget can fulfil its prime function if, firstly, the elements of risk are identified and expressed within it and, secondly, if the budget is properly assigned another of its potential functions; that is, the provision of particular, staged, financial aims, the following of which will, if strategically monitored and reconciled, result in the achievement of the project's final, budgeted objective. Project risk can be managed provided that its extent is quantified or presented in some way in the budget so as to facilitate the vital cost management function of monitoring, reconciling and amending the project's budget elements as actual costs become known. The two elements of this requirement, the quantification and presentation of risk and cost management are each now considered in turn.

7.2   QUANTIFICATION AND PRESENTATION OF RISK IN THE DEVELOPMENT BUDGET

All the elements of a conventional development budget will be forecasts in the form of single point, financial amounts – that is, absolute, apparently precise sums. For example, the building cost, forecast by the methods described in Chapter 5, will be presented as such a sum. But inherent in these methods, as described, is the characteristic of the single point sum being derived from within a range of values, from a possible maximum to minimum cost, which can be given a greater value of certainty as the range is extended. An expert, building cost forecaster could not be certain of a single point forecast cost given at the inception stage of the project, but would probably claim certainty for the cost eventually falling within a forecast range of costs. This applies not only to building cost forecasts, but equally to forecasts of land price, income, rent, yields, inflation rates and any other required budget element.

Ideally, then, a budget would most meaningfully consist of amounts not as single point amounts but as ranges from maximum to minimum, with the various results, in terms of feasibility, being expressed on the basis of the combination of the range possibilities. Such techniques have been developed and are used for general investment appraisal calculations. However, the multiplicity of the items and the complexity of their occurrence profile in building developments limits their use in this particular sphere in the comprehensive form described. But a meaningful development budget requires some feature of quantification of possible variations from its single point forecast amounts, and the presentation of the effects of these variations with some statistical expression of the probability of the occurrence of the various feasibility values that would be obtained.

The following sections consider the general technique of statistical probability and its application in simulation and sensitivity analysis, with particular reference to how these may be applied to a development budget.

7.2.1 Statistical Probability

The basis of statistical probability theory is the assignment of a numerical value (P) to the probability of the occurrence of a defined event. The numerical P-value assigned is expressed as a number within the range of 0–1 or 0–100% with 0 or 0% representing *nil* probability of the occurrence and 1 or 100% representing *certainty* of the occurrence.

The value is derived from the relative frequency of the occurrence – that is, the relationship between the number of actual and potential occurrences. This can be expressed in the following formula:

P-value for the occurrence of event X = number of actual occurrences of event X ÷ potential possible occurrences of event X

The data for the number of actual and potential occurrences necessary for the calculation of the P-value can be derived in the following ways:

(1) Logical inference
This is the deduction, based on logic, of the numbers of occurrences from the nature of the events. For example, the P-value for the event of a six-sided, 1–6 numbered dice being thrown and landing with an exposed 6 can be logically inferred to be:

$$\frac{1}{6} = 0.167 \ (16.7\%)$$

Similarly, for the event of a tossed coin landing on heads, the P-value, logically inferred is:

$$\frac{1}{2} = 0.5 \ (50\%)$$

The above values, that is, 1 occurrence of a six in every 6 dice throws and 1 occurrence of a head in every 2 coin tosses, were derived from logical deduction based on the nature of a dice and a coin. Many occurrences requiring a probability value, including the accuracy of development budget forecasts, do not possess characteristics which allow deduction.

(2) Empirical observation

The *P*-value can be deduced from the observation and recording of the number of actual and potential events. For example, the *P*-value of the occurrence of a dice being thrown to 6 can be calculated by observation and recording of a series of dice throws, and the observed number of thrown 6s in the series being divided by the total number of throws in the series.

An empirical observation will usually consist, particularly in regard to elements in a development budget, of historical data relating to the occurrences of the event being considered.

The technique of assigning *P*-values can usefully be applied in development budget situations by calculating the probability value of budget forecast amounts being within a given range of accuracy.

An illustration of this is Table 7.1, which is a record of the accuracy of 20 building cost forecasts and the calculation from this data of the probability (*P*) of a future forecast being within specified ranges of accuracy.

The first column of Table 7.1 gives the number of forecasts that were within the percentage range of accuracy stated in the second column. In the third column is the *P*-value for a forecast being of the relevant percentage accuracy, and this is calculated by dividing the number of forecasts in the first column by the total forecasts, that is, 20. The last column gives the cumulative *P*-value, that is the *P*-value for the forecast being within the range of accuracy represented by the total percentage

Table 7.1   Probability of accuracy of building cost forecast

No. of Forecasts (Total = 20)	Accuracy ± %	Probability P (%)	Cumulative Probability P (%)
1	1	0.05 (5)	0.05 (5)
2	2	0.10 (10)	0.15 (15)
3	3	0.15 (15)	0.30 (30)
3	4	0.15 (15)	0.45 (45)
9	5	0.45 (45)	0.90 (90)
1	6	0.05 (5)	0.95 (95)
1	7	0.05 (5)	1.00 (100)

accuracy. For example, the probability of the forecast being within ±4% accuracy is 0.45P (45%). The data gives a statistical certainty of the forecast being within ±7%!

The range of forecast amounts with probability values for the likelihood of the actual amount being at certain points within this range that is produced by the above technique can be utilised in a development budget. A range of feasibility results can be produced for a range of costs for a particular cost item. A probability value can be given for the feasibility result range and for the result being at a particular point within the range.

This application is illustrated using an example of a project for which the budget items (simplified) are as follows:

Example project A: Budget details

	£ million
FORECAST COSTS	
Land acquisition (present value)	0.25
Building cost (present value)	0.75
Finance (1% of PV of other costs)	0.01
FORECAST VALUE	
Realisable in project Year 2	1.20

The probability values calculated in Table 7.1 for the accuracy of the building cost forecast can be used to prepare a range of rates of return for the project. This is illustrated in Table 7.2.

The first row of Table 7.2 gives the rate of return, 9%, for the project based on the budgeted, single amount forecasts. The following rows

Table 7.2   Rates of return for variable building costs

	Building Cost (variable) £million	Land Cost (constant) £million	Finance Cost 1% £million	Total £million	Rate of Return (% discounts £1.2 million to total cost)
Forecast	0.7500	0.2500	0.0100	1.0100	9.0
+7%	0.8025	0.2500	0.0105	1.0630	6.25
−7%	0.6975	0.2500	0.0095	0.9570	11.75
+3%	0.7725	0.2500	0.0102	1.0327	7.75
−3%	0.7275	0.2500	0.0098	0.9873	10.25

give the rates of return that would be achieved for varied values of building cost. From this, based on the probability of accuracy of the building cost forecast as produced in Table 7.1, it can be concluded that the project will produce a rate of return within the range of 6.25–11.75% and for this, the probability value is statistical certainty. This range of rate of return is calculated in rows 2 and 3, which are based on a 7% variation to the building cost forecast, for which there is a probability value of 1.0 (100%) in Table 7.1.

Ranges of rates of return of more limited extent can be produced based on the probability in Table 7.1. For example, rates of return have been calculated for building costs varying 3% from the forecast figure (rows 4 and 5). These produce a range of rate of return of 7.75–10.25% and the probability of the rate being within this range is 0.3 (30%).

The presentation of ranges of feasibility and their probability values as described, together with the development budget in single point forecast form, provide a potentially very useful technique, which goes some way to quantifying an identified risk and can therefore be of meaningful assistance to a developer's decision on feasibility. However, the application of the technique does have certain difficulties.

Firstly, many of the items in the development budget may not be susceptible to the assignment of a probability value of their accuracy owing to the lack of reliable, empirically derived, statistical data on occurrences of accuracy of forecasts. To some extent this can be overcome by using, not empirical, statistical data, but subjective judgement on the likely accuracy of a forecast. An expert, professional cost forecaster could normally be expected to produce a range of costs with an intuitive assessment, translated into a *P*-value, of the likelihood of the actual cost being at certain points within the range. It can be argued that the expert process of forecasting, traditionally founded on the principle of single point, amount forecasts, is inconsistent with the techniques of range and statistical probability. This can be illustrated by the paradox in the probabilities produced in Table 7.1, in which the probability of the forecast being correct, in the sense of within ±1%, is less that 0.05 (5%).

A second disadvantage, apparent in the way the method was presented above, is that it accounts for inaccuracy in cost forecast of only one budget element. Although various ranges of rate of return can be calculated for all cost elements, each one will be on the basis that one element was variable and all the others constant. This is unlikely. The production of ranges of rates of return based on variability of all the budget elements would require a quantity of calculation that could only be performed in a realistic time by a computer. Such a computer technique is considered in section 7.2.3.

7.2.2 Sensitivity Analysis

The method of sensitivity analysis consists of the identification and analysis of particular budget elements which are particularly crucial for project feasibility, and quantifying and presenting the level of this sensitivity of the elements for the project's rate of return. The techniques are based on the statistical range theories described in section 7.2.1 above.

The method requires the calculation of the effect on the rate of return of adverse changes to the forecast amount of the individual budget elements, and thus identifying those which require detailed consideration by the developer in making the decision on whether or not to undertake the project. This also allows the identification of those elements which require close management cost monitoring as they are realised, if the project does proceed.

The calculation of the effects on the rate of return is carried out on the basis described in Chapter 6 and illustrated in Table 7.1. The results of these calculations can be most meaningfully represented graphically in a sensitivity diagram.

The diagram in Appendix A to this chapter is a sensitivity diagram which graphically represents the effects of a variation in building cost on the rate of return of the project. The project is that defined in Example project A, and for which rate of return ranges were calculated in Table 7.2.

The diagram also shows the same effects for a change in land acquisition costs. The calculation of these effects is shown in Table 7.3.

The significance of the representation of the sensitivity of individual budget elements in the graphical form given in Appendix A to this chapter is that it clearly identifies the relative sensitivity of different elements. A cost represented on a graph of this form will be more sensitive in relation to the rate of return, the closer its line is to the horizontal axis. On which basis it can be seen from the graph that, in

Table 7.3   Rates of return for variable land costs

	Land Cost (variable) £million	Building Cost (constant) £million	Finance Cost 1% £million	Total £million	Rate of Return (% discounts £1.2 million to total costs)
Forecast	0.2500	0.7500	0.0100	1.0100	9.00
+10%	0.2750	0.7500	0.0103	1.0353	7.75
−10%	0.225	0.7500	0.0098	0.9848	10.25

the circumstances of that project, variations in building cost would have a relatively greater effect on project rate of return than variations to land acquisition costs.

7.2.3 Simulation Technique

Simulation techniques applied in investment and cost analysis are the testing of forecasts by varying, in random fashion, the elements of the analysis to produce a range of feasibility results. The performance of the large number of calculations required to produce a statistically significant number of variable cost combinations requires a computer program. The best developed of these is the Monte Carlo simulation.

The application of such a system to a development budget involves the following processes:

(1) Identification and statistical classification of variable budget elements
The variable elements in the budget, that is, those which are not yet realised and require to be forecast, are identified, and the statistical profiles of their respective variabilities are ascertained. This profile consists of the element's minimum, maximum and mean values and standard deviation. The techniques for forecasting these are based on the methods of deriving data for probability calculations described in section 7.2.1. The difficulties of this for development budget forecasts described there will apply in this process.
(2) Calculation of possible rates of return
This is the process carried out by the application of a computer program to choose random budget element values, in accordance with the statistical profile of the elements identified in stage (1). The number of random variables used will be determined by the number of computer runs undertaken.

The process will produce a series of rates of return for the project with a statistical analysis of these which identifies the mean and mode return and the likely number of returns which vary from these.
(3) Project decision
The decision on whether or not to undertake the project is based on the consideration of the range of rates of return and their statistical analysis produced by stage (2).

7.3 MANAGEMENT OF RISK

The techniques described in section 7.2 are attempts to quantify and present in the development budget identified risks, with the aim of providing more comprehensive information on which the developer can base the decision of whether or not to proceed with the project.

The assignment of probability values and the analysis of sensitivity might constitute adequate presentation of risk, but they do not effectively quantify it in a way that materially alters the budget. They are useful and essential adjuncts to the budget, not an integral part of it.

A fully developed simulation model would constitute the quantification of risk, as the statistical profile of the randomly derived models could, in itself, constitute a budget. However, simulation techniques rely, as do probability values and sensitivity analysis, on the existence of data of sufficient quality to produce values and analyses that are statistically valid. The elements of a typical development budget might not have such data and thus reliance has to be placed upon subjective assessment. In this situation such methods may have no great advantage over a budget consisting of single point amount forecasts, which have been expertly derived.

This advantage of the single point forecast budget is strengthened if it is provided with an identification of sensitive elements, with some form of analysis and quantification of the extent of their sensitivity. It is strengthened even further if the amounts of the budget are viewed as targets and are monitored, reconciled and amended, that is, effectively cost-managed. There are some essential features of effective cost management of a building project, and these are particularly vital with respect to cost targets which have been identified as sensitive for the fulfilment of the project's cost aim. These features are now considered.

(1) Inclusion of contingency
A sum can be included in the budgeted costs for use when amendment is required to compensate for a cost overrun in a budget cost. In principle, a contingency could be viewed as poor budgeting, since the requirement of a project budget is the exhaustive identification of cost factors and the realistic, that is, achievable, forecast of their amount. However if the amount of the contingency is properly assessed in relation to the sensitivity of the cost items, it can be an effective management tool. Its expenditure should be closely monitored, as part of the essential, overall monitoring process, and related to the progress of the project and realisation of actual costs.

(2) Cost monitoring
This must be carried out constantly, starting at an early stage. All indications of a variation between actual and forecast cost should be considered, and appropriate actions taken. Chapter 3, section 3.4 described the scope for cost-amending action under the various types of procurement systems.

(3) Building cost planning at design stage
As shown above, building cost is usually the largest single element of cost and the most significant. The die for building cost is cast at the design stage, so it is vital for an effective cost planning and control

procedure to be used at this stage, with full cognisance of the budgeted, that is targeted, building cost. Design cost planning and control procedures are beyond the scope of this book, but their development and more effective and comprehensive use are essential.

7.4 FURTHER READING

Byrne P. and Cadman D., *Risk, Uncertainty and Decision Making in Property Development*. Spon, 1984.

Cuming M., *Quantitative Methods: A Manager's Guide*, 2nd edn. ELM, 1992.

Ferry D.J. and Brandon P.S., *Cost Planning of Buildings*, 6th edn, Chapters 14–19. BSP, 1991.

Flanagan R. and Stevens S., 'Risk analysis', in *Quantity Surveying Techniques: New Directions* (Ed. Brandon P.S.). BSP, 1988.

Flanagan R., *Risk Management and Construction*. BSP, 1990.

Pilcher R., *Project Cost Control in Construction*, Chapter 4. BSP, 1985.

Seeley I.H., *Building Economics*, 3rd edn. The Macmillan Press, 1983.

APPENDIX A TO CHAPTER 7: SENSITIVITY GRAPH – EFFECT ON RATE OF RETURN OF VARIATION TO FORECASTS

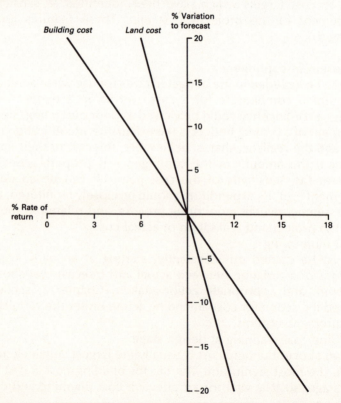

Appendix: Compounding and Discounting Tables

1. Amount of £1
2. Present Value of £1
3. Amount of £1 per Period
4. Present Value of £1 per Period

1. AMOUNT OF £1

For rates of interest (i) and for periods (n) $= (1 + i)^n$

Rates of Interest

Periods	3%	4%	5%	6%	7%	8%	9%	10%
1	1.0300	1.0400	1.0500	1.0600	1.0700	1.0800	1.0900	1.1000
2	1.0609	1.0816	1.1025	1.1236	1.1449	1.1664	1.1881	1.2100
3	1.0927	1.1249	1.1576	1.1910	1.2250	1.2597	1.2950	1.3310
4	1.1255	1.1699	1.2155	1.2625	1.3108	1.3605	1.4116	1.4641
5	1.1593	1.2167	1.2763	1.3382	1.4026	1.4693	1.5386	1.6105
6	1.1941	1.2653	1.3401	1.4185	1.5007	1.5869	1.6771	1.7716
7	1.2299	1.3159	1.4071	1.5036	1.6058	1.7138	1.8280	1.9487
8	1.2668	1.3686	1.4775	1.5938	1.7182	1.8509	1.9926	2.1436
9	1.3048	1.4233	1.5513	1.6895	1.8385	1.9990	2.1719	2.3579
10	1.3439	1.4802	1.6289	1.7908	1.9672	2.1589	2.3674	2.5937
15	1.5580	1.8009	2.0789	2.3966	2.7590	3.1722	3.6425	4.1772
20	1.8061	2.1911	2.6533	3.2071	3.8697	4.6610	5.6044	6.7275
25	2.0938	2.6658	3.3864	4.2919	5.4274	6.8485	8.6231	10.8347
30	2.4273	3.2434	4.3219	5.7435	7.6123	10.0627	13.2677	17.4494
35	2.8139	3.9461	5.5160	7.6861	10.6766	14.7853	20.4140	28.1024
40	3.2620	4.8010	7.0400	10.2857	14.9745	21.7245	31.4094	45.2593
45	3.7816	5.8412	8.9850	13.7646	21.0025	31.9204	48.3273	72.8905
50	4.3839	7.1067	11.4674	18.4202	29.4570	46.9016	74.3575	117.391
55	5.0821	8.6464	14.6356	24.6503	41.3150	68.9139	114.408	189.059
60	5.8916	10.5196	18.6792	32.9877	57.9464	101.257	176.031	304.482
65	6.8300	12.7987	23.8399	44.1450	81.2729	148.780	270.846	490.371
70	7.9178	15.5716	30.4264	59.0759	113.989	218.606	416.730	789.747
75	9.1789	18.9453	38.8327	79.0569	159.876	321.205	641.191	1271.90
80	10.6409	23.0498	49.5614	105.796	224.234	471.935	986.552	2048.40
90	14.3005	34.1193	80.7304	189.464	441.103	1018.92	2335.53	5313.02
100	19.2186	50.5049	131.5013	339.302	867.716	2199.76	5529.04	13780.6

2. PRESENT VALUE OF £1

For rates of interest (*i*) and for periods (*n*) = $\dfrac{1}{(1+i)^n}$

Rates of Interest

Periods	3%	4%	5%	6%	7%	8%	9%	10%
1	0.97087	0.96154	0.95238	0.94340	0.93458	0.92593	0.91743	0.90909
2	0.94260	0.92456	0.90703	0.89000	0.87344	0.85734	0.84168	0.82645
3	0.91514	0.88900	0.86384	0.83962	0.81630	0.79383	0.77218	0.75131
4	0.88849	0.85480	0.82270	0.79209	0.76290	0.73503	0.70843	0.68301
5	0.86261	0.82193	0.78353	0.74726	0.71299	0.68058	0.64993	0.62092
6	0.83748	0.79031	0.74622	0.70496	0.66634	0.63017	0.59627	0.56447
7	0.81309	0.75992	0.71068	0.66506	0.62275	0.58349	0.54703	0.51316
8	0.78941	0.73069	0.67684	0.62741	0.58201	0.54027	0.50187	0.46651
9	0.76642	0.70259	0.64461	0.59190	0.54393	0.50025	0.46043	0.42410
10	0.74409	0.67556	0.61391	0.55839	0.50835	0.46319	0.42241	0.38554
15	0.64186	0.55526	0.48102	0.41727	0.36245	0.31524	0.27454	0.23939
20	0.55368	0.45639	0.37689	0.31180	0.25842	0.21455	0.17843	0.14864
25	0.47761	0.37512	0.29530	0.23300	0.18425	0.14602	0.11597	0.09230
30	0.41199	0.30832	0.23138	0.17411	0.13137	0.09938	0.07537	0.05731
35	0.35538	0.25342	0.18129	0.13011	0.09366	0.06763	0.04899	0.03558
40	0.30656	0.20829	0.14205	0.09722	0.06678	0.04603	0.03184	0.02209
45	0.26444	0.17120	0.11130	0.07265	0.04761	0.03133	0.02069	0.01372
50	0.22811	0.14071	0.08720	0.05429	0.03395	0.02132	0.01345	0.00852
55	0.19677	0.11566	0.06833	0.04057	0.02420	0.01451	0.00874	0.00529
60	0.16973	0.09506	0.05354	0.03031	0.01726	0.00988	0.00568	0.00328
65	0.14641	0.07813	0.04195	0.02265	0.01230	0.00672	0.00369	0.00204
70	0.12630	0.06422	0.03287	0.01693	0.00877	0.00457	0.00240	0.00127
75	0.10895	0.05278	0.02575	0.01265	0.00625	0.00311	0.00156	0.00079
80	0.09398	0.04338	0.02018	0.00945	0.00446	0.00212	0.00101	0.00049
90	0.06993	0.02931	0.01239	0.00528	0.00227	0.00098	0.00043	0.00019
100	0.05203	0.01980	0.00760	0.00295	0.00115	0.00045	0.00018	0.00007

3. AMOUNT OF £1 PER PERIOD

For rates of interest (i) and for periods (n) = $\dfrac{(1+i)^n - 1}{1}$

Rates of Interest

Periods	3%	4%	5%	6%	7%	8%	9%	10%
1	1.0000	1.0000	1.0000	1.0000	1.0000	1.0000	1.0000	1.0000
2	2.0300	2.0400	2.0500	2.0600	2.0700	2.0800	2.0900	2.1000
3	3.0900	3.1216	3.1525	3.1836	3.2149	3.2464	3.2781	3.3100
4	4.1836	4.2465	4.3101	4.3746	4.4399	4.5061	4.5731	4.6410
5	5.3091	5.4163	5.5256	5.6371	5.7507	5.8666	5.9847	6.1051
6	6.4684	6.6330	6.8019	6.9753	7.1533	7.3359	7.5233	7.7156
7	7.6625	7.8983	8.1420	8.3938	8.6540	8.9228	9.2004	9.4872
8	8.8923	9.2142	9.5491	9.8975	10.2598	10.6366	11.0285	11.4359
9	10.1591	10.5828	11.0266	11.4913	11.9780	12.4876	13.0210	13.5795
10	11.4639	12.0061	12.5779	13.1808	13.8164	14.4866	15.1929	15.9374
20	26.8704	29.7781	33.0660	36.7856	40.9955	45.7620	51.1601	57.2750
30	47.5754	56.0849	66.4388	79.0582	94.4608	113.283	136.308	164.494
40	75.4013	95.0255	120.800	154.762	199.635	259.057	337.882	442.593
50	112.797	152.667	209.348	290.336	406.529	573.770	815.084	1163.91
60	163.053	237.991	353.584	533.128	813.520	1253.21	1944.79	3034.82
70	230.594	364.291	588.529	967.932	1614.13	2720.08	4619.22	7887.47
80	321.363	551.245	971.229	1746.60	3189.06	5886.94	10950.6	20474.0
90	443.349	827.983	1594.61	3141.08	6287.19	12723.9	25939.2	53120.2
100	607.288	1237.62	2610.03	5638.37	12381.7	27484.5	61422.7	137796.0

4. PRESENT VALUE OF £1 PER PERIOD

For rates of interest (i) and for periods (n) = $\dfrac{(1+i)^n - 1}{i(1+i)^n}$

Rates of Interest

Periods	3%	4%	5%	6%	7%	8%	9%	10%
1	0.9709	0.9615	0.9524	0.9434	0.9346	0.9259	0.9174	0.9091
2	1.9135	1.8861	1.8594	1.8334	1.8080	1.7833	1.7591	1.7355
3	2.8286	2.7751	2.7232	2.6730	2.6243	2.5771	2.5313	2.4869
4	3.7171	3.6299	3.5460	3.4651	3.3872	3.3121	3.2397	3.1699
5	4.5797	4.4518	4.3295	4.2124	4.1002	3.9927	3.8897	3.7908
6	5.4172	5.2421	5.0757	4.9173	4.7665	4.6229	4.4859	4.3553
7	6.2303	6.0021	5.7864	5.5824	5.3893	5.2064	5.0330	4.8684
8	7.0197	6.7327	6.4632	6.2098	5.9713	5.7466	5.5348	5.3349
9	7.7861	7.4353	7.1078	6.8017	6.5152	6.2469	5.9952	5.7590
10	8.5302	8.1109	7.7217	7.3601	7.0236	6.7101	6.4177	6.1446
20	14.878	13.590	12.462	11.470	10.594	9.8181	9.1285	8.5136
30	19.600	17.292	15.373	13.765	12.409	11.258	10.274	9.4269
40	23.115	19.793	17.159	15.046	13.332	11.925	10.757	9.7791
50	25.730	21.482	18.256	15.762	13.801	12.234	10.962	9.9148
60	27.676	22.624	18.929	16.161	14.039	12.377	11.048	9.9672
70	29.123	23.395	19.342	16.385	14.160	12.443	11.084	9.9873
80	30.201	23.915	19.597	16.509	14.222	12.474	11.100	9.9951
90	31.002	24.267	19.752	16.579	14.253	12.488	11.106	9.9981
100	31.559	24.505	19.848	16.618	14.269	12.494	11.109	9.9993
Perp.	33.333	25.000	20.000	16.667	14.286	12.500	11.111	10.000

Index

accountant 2
all-in discount rate 81
alteration work 2, 70–1
appraisal 2, 40
approximate quantity price forecast 69
architect 20, 23

balance
  of budget 78
  of present value 78–83
  of value and cost 78
borrowing 81
budget *see* development budget
budget targets 3
building
  appraisal 40
  cost 1, 2, 53, 56–63, 79, 90
  cost factors 58–61
  cost forecast 63–71, 90
  function 39, 64–5
  method 58
  overhead costs 60
  price 57, 61–3
  profit 61–2
  project 2
  quality 59
  quantities 58–9
  regulation approval 18
  resource costs 57–61, 80
  surveyor 2
Building Cost Information Service
  standard cost analysis 69
  tender price index 69
business organisation 42, 45

capital gains tax 48
capital reserves 81
capital value 2, 30, 41, 43, 44, 46
capitalised income value 30, 35–7, 41,
    43, 44, 46, 82
cash flow 9, 55, 81
civil engineering works 2
commissioning 19–20, 51, 54

community charge 49
comparable sale value 30–2, 41, 43, 44,
    46, 82
competitive tender 21, 23, 61
compounding 10–15
construction
  cost 21, 51, 53–4
  process 21
  stage 18
construction management 24, 28
contingency 97
contractor 21
corporation tax 48
cost 1, 2, 3, 6, 7, 21, 36, 51–71, 90
  factors 58–61
  limit 7
  management 3, 7, 8, 9, 15, 25–8,
      37, 95
  monitoring 97
  planning 97
  schedule 79, 81
council tax 49
current capital value 30, 33–5, 41, 43,
    44, 46, 82

decision to build 1, 17–18
demolition 53
design
  constraints 40
  elements 69
  fees 21, 53
  stage 19
design/build 21–3, 26
developer 1, 47, 85
development
  budget 3, 5, 7, 15, 78
  process 2, 17–28
  situations 41–6
  value 7
discounted cash flow 15
discounting 10–15

electrical engineer 21

elemental price forecast   69
empirical observation   93
environmental quality   2
external works   71

facilities manager   2
feasibility   77–88
finance cost   2, 51, 54–5
financial analyst   2
financial appraisal   2, 3
  computer programs   3
  integration of techniques   2, 3
floor area cost forecast   64–8
forecast   8, 89, 91
  building price   63–71
  cost   5, 79
  value   5
future compounded amount   10

general building contractor   *see*
    contractor
gross internal floor area (GIFA)   64–5

inception stage   5, 17, 79
income   36, 42, 45–6
income tax   48
inflation   15–16
interest rate   9, 15, 54, 55, 81
interim valuation   79, 80–1

labour cost   57
land acquisition   18, 51, 52, 56
local taxation   49
logical inference   91–2

maintenance work   2, 20
management   3, 53, 96–8
management contracting   23–4, 28
market conditions   39
market value   30–1, 62–3
mark-up   61
material cost   57
mechanical engineer   21

occupancy cost   2, 36
operating income   36, 42, 45–6
opportunity cost   55

P-value   91–2
planning permission   18, 53
plant cost   57
present value   10, 78, 79, 82
price   6, 57, 61–3
probability   91–4
procurement methods   18, 20–5
  construction management   24, 28
  design/build   21–3, 26
  effect on project cost   24–5, 57

effect on project management   25–8
  management contracting   23–4, 28
  traditional   20–1
profit   61–2, *see also* rate of return
profit-making organisation   45, 78
programme   79
project
  capital value   2, 30, 41, 43, 44, 46
  capitalised income value   30, 35–7, 41,
    43, 44, 46, 82
  comparable sale value   30–2, 41, 43,
    44, 46, 82
  cost   3, 6, 7, 36, 51–71
  cost management   3, 7, 8, 9, 15, 25–8,
    37
  cost schedule   79, 81
  current capital value   30, 33–5, 41, 43,
    44, 82
  feasibility   77–8
  finance   2
  inception stage   5
  management   3, 53, 96–8
  operating income   36, 42, 45–6
  programme   79
  revenue   2
  risk   89–98
  target value   30, 37–40, 43, 44, 46, 82
  value   3, 6, 29–49
    effect of taxation   47–9
    methods of calculating   40–7
  viability   1, 2, 5, 7
property
  developer   41
  market   30
  valuer   2, 29

quantities   58–9
quantity surveyor   2, 21

rate of return   33, 55, 78, 81, 83–5, 94
rates   49
refurbishment work   2
relocation cost   51, 52
repair work   2, 20
residual valuation   7, 77
resource costs   57–61, 80
retention   81
revenue   2
risk   6, 89–98
  analysis   90–8
  of building price   62
  in forecasts   8
  quantification   8, 62, 90–6

S-curve   80
sale value   30–2, 35–7, 41, 43, 44, 46, 82
schedule of costs   79

sensitivity analysis 95–6
simulation technique 96
site preparation 53
stage payments 79, 80–1
Standard Method of Measurement, 7th
    edition 58
statistical probability 91–4
structural engineer 21
sub-contractors *see* works contractors

target value 30, 37–40, 41, 43, 44, 46, 82
taxation 47–9, 51, 55
time effect on budget 7, 9–15, 78–9

traditional procurement 20–1

uncertainty 89, *see also* risk

value 3, 6, 29–49
    effect of taxation 47–9
    methods of calculating 40–7
value added tax 49, 55
variations 25, 26
viability 1, 2, 5, 7

works contractors 21, 23, 24

yield 33